He had it all wo

Was this how he ...
Making spur-of-the-...
ing other people, co...
with his plans. . .?

'I—I don't have anything suitable to wear,'
she argued, and realised, with horror, that she
was teetering on the edge of giving in.

'I can't believe that. You might like to pack
an evening dress, though. . .there's a dinner
dance the night we arrive.'

'If I do fly up to the resort with you, I'll expect
you to keep a dance for me,' she heard herself
declaring recklessly.

'That's a promise.' He leaned back, a satisfied
smile on his lips. He was quite ruthless, she
realised. Ruthless in getting what he wanted.

Elizabeth Duke was brought up in the foothills of Adelaide, South Australia, but has lived in Melbourne ever since her marriage to husband John. She trained as a librarian and has worked in various libraries over the years. These days she only works one day a week, as a medical librarian, which gives her time to do what she loves doing most—writing. She also enjoys researching her books and travelling with her husband in Australia and overseas. Their two grown-up children are now married.

Recent titles by the same author:

HEARTLESS STRANGER

TAKEOVER ENGAGEMENT

BY
ELIZABETH DUKE

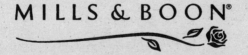

All the characters in this book have no existence outside the imagination of the author, and have no relation whatsoever to anyone bearing the same name or names. They are not even distantly inspired by any individual known or unknown to the author, and all the incidents are pure invention.

First published in Great Britain 1997
Harlequin Mills & Boon Limited,
Eton House, 18–24 Paradise Road, Richmond, Surrey TW9 1SR

© Elizabeth Duke 1997

ISBN 0 263 80038 5

Set in 10 on 10½ pt Linotron Times
02-9703-62661-D

Typeset in Great Britain by CentraCet, Cambridge
Printed and bound in Great Britain
by Mackays of Chatham PLC, Chatham

CHAPTER ONE

LUCY glanced at her watch as she hurried across the tiled lobby to the lifts. Two minutes to twelve. She was cutting things a bit too fine.

It was an old building, one of the oldest in Melbourne. The two lifts looked as if they were from the same era, judging by the heavy doors and the ancient iron numbers on the panel above. An amber light showed that one lift was stationary on the top floor—the sixth. The other was slowly, ever so slowly descending.

Time was ticking away. She began to tap her foot. Would that darned lift never come? David would think she was doing this deliberately. . .making him wait until the last possible moment. . .teasing him by showing up just in the nick of time. David, I wouldn't do that to you, she told him silently. I meant to be early. . .truly.

She felt a twinge of guilt. Then why hadn't she left the clinic earlier and made *allowances* for any possible delays, like traffic jams?

Approaching footsteps diverted her. As she turned her head a beam of sunlight from the front entrance of the old building caught her face in its harsh autumn glow.

She would have sworn she heard a sharp intake of breath from the man who had paused a few paces away from her, a tall, dark-haired man in a charcoal-grey suit.

For the briefest second their eyes met, vibrant turquoise clashing with heart-stopping, depthless black. With the daylight behind him, the man's face was shadowed, yet even so she could sense his interest in her, his almost startled reaction, his lips parting as if he were about to speak. Then he clamped his mouth shut and flicked his gaze away, as if realising he'd mistaken her for someone else.

She felt an involuntary tremor run through her as she turned back to the lifts. There was something about the man. . .some potent force about him that she found. . .disturbing. Even that single brief glance had been enough to tell her that here was a successful, supremely self-confident, possibly powerful man. A man who would despise weakness and failure—in himself as much as in others. He didn't strike her as the kind of man who would easily make a mistake.

A *ding* from above signalled the arrival of the lift. At last! She looked at her watch and swore under her breath. Five past twelve! She was five minutes late already. Damn!

The heavy doors rattled open and she stepped inside, the fine hairs at her nape prickling as the dark-eyed stranger followed her in.

Without looking at him, she extended a finger and pressed the button marked '6' before melting back against the wall to allow him access to the panel. He merely inclined his head and moved back a step, to stand with his back against the opposite wall. Facing her, she noted, rather than the door.

She willed herself not to react, or look directly at him. But as the doors clanged shut and the lift began its slow grinding ascent she found herself watching him out of the corner of her eye. Feeling his eyes on her again.

For the first time she felt a twinge of unease. Had he really been heading for the sixth floor, or had he only decided to do so after seeing that she was going there herself? With the rate this lift was moving it could take an age to get there. Was he aware of that?

Suddenly she felt glaringly vulnerable and alone. It was unlikely that the lift would stop on its way up to collect any other passengers. Anyone waiting on the upper floors of the building would be more likely to be waiting to come *down*.

She swallowed hard. It wouldn't be the first time a lone woman had been attacked in a lift. And this man looked extremely strong, extremely powerful. If he lunged at her she wouldn't have a chance.

On the other hand, he looked far too smooth and self-possessed, far too well-dressed and respectable to be a potential rapist. But there was no point in taking any chances.

She stiffened her jaw and turned her body slightly away from his, facing the lift door—hoping that her body language would send out off-putting signals.

Glancing at the panel in front of her, she noted that they were slowly approaching the third floor. Barely halfway!

If she hadn't been feeling so edgy, with David's ultimatum at the back of her mind and this disturbing stranger adding to her nervous tension, she might have seen the amusing side of this interminable lift ride and shared a wry smile with her fellow passenger.

But she didn't dare. Even though she wasn't directly facing him now, she knew—she just *knew*—that he was still looking at *her*.

It wasn't that she'd never had a man stare at her before. Her eyes, being such an intense blue, tended to attract attention—from men in particular—though in her own opinion they were spaced too widely apart. And her hair, which was long and straight, except for a slight curl where it swirled round her shoulders, was an unusual colour too, she guessed. People had described it at various times as rich chestnut, deep honey, even as burnt gold. . .it seemed to change with the light.

Her figure wasn't too bad either, thanks to all the bike-riding, swimming and running she did. On the other hand her nose was too long, her mouth far too large and her lips too full. 'Kissable lips', David had called them once, but then, he was biased. As for her neck. . .well, swans weren't in it!

Still, whatever she looked like, she didn't deserve to be eyed in the way this stranger was eyeing her. Never before had she been so pricklingly aware of a man's scrutiny, so. . .confused by it. She didn't know whether to find it flattering, irritating, tiresome. . .or alarming.

From her own fleeting appraisal of him, he didn't look the type of man who would stand and stare at a woman, even surreptitiously. He looked more the type who would be used to being stared *at*.

Which she was tempted to do. . .and she just might have risked a quick glance if she hadn't felt so alone and exposed, stuck in this confined space with him. Instead, she darted another anxious peek at her watch. And at the same moment the lift gave a ghastly jolt.

Her darkly fringed eyes sprang wide, her gaze colliding with the narrowed black eyes of the stranger opposite. She gave a weak smile, holding her breath as the lift gave another frightening jolt before coming to a shuddering halt.

Her eyes leapt to the numbered panel. 'Oh, no,' she groaned aloud. They were stuck between the fifth and sixth floors! So near and yet so far.

'About time they installed some new lifts,' her companion commented drily, and, despite her alarm, she noted how deep and softly vibrant his voice was. It seemed to coil right down into the pit of her stomach.

She caught her breath as he lunged forward suddenly, his hand shooting out to press button '6' on the panel. She almost had to catch her breath all over again as a waft of his aftershave drifted past her nostrils. Not that it was strong—it was extremely subtle, extremely. . .well, *male. Disturbingly* male. As *he* was, she realised, headily aware of his close proximity. . .his tall, athletic physique. . .his strong, chiselled face. . . those eyes.

'Damn!' he swore when nothing happened. He

pressed another button, then another, stabbing at each one with an increasingly vicious finger. 'Come on, damn it. . .move!'

'What are we going to do?' she burst out, alarm mingling with dismay. David wasn't going to wait for her. Well, not for much longer. He'd warned her. If she didn't turn up by twelve-fifteen at the very latest he was leaving. And he would too. He had an afternoon plane to catch.

'This is the last time I'm going to ask you, Lu,' he'd pronounced only yesterday. 'I've waited long enough. If you don't turn up tomorrow, I'll know your answer. That'll be it. It'll be over.'

He'd meant it too. She'd never seen him more decisive. And she couldn't blame him. She'd kept him dangling for far too long. Even elastic could only stretch so far.

Why did I leave it so late to drive into town? she berated herself. And why didn't I run up the stairs when I saw the lift was taking so long to come? What's six flights of stairs when your future's at stake?

She felt a wave of mingled mortification and panic. She'd taken David too much for granted. Expecting him always to be there, patiently waiting. . .waiting until she was ready to make up her mind, to make a commitment. She had been so unfair to him!

For the first time she paused to think about what she might be losing if she missed today's appointment with him. She'd be losing one of the gentlest, most decent, most dependable men a girl could ever hope to find. Was she *crazy*?

'Can't you *do* something?' she cried. 'I'm supposed to be meeting someone at twelve!'

The man turned his head, his mouth quirking into a crooked smile which, despite its mockery, was startlingly sensual. 'He'll wait, won't he?' The black eyes raked over her.

A surge of heat scorched up her slender neck. She

clutched her handbag to her chest in an instinctively protective gesture, feeling suddenly stripped bare.

Despite the predicament they were in, and despite her fevered wariness, she found herself covertly examining his face from under her fringe of thick lashes, trying to work out just what it was about him that she found so disturbing.

His face was lean and hard, slashed with cynical lines on either side of his square jaw. His sensual mouth had a sardonic twist. His hair was very dark, almost black, its wiry thickness tamed by a stylish cut. But there was nothing tame about him. She only had to look into the glittering black eyes to sense that. He exuded a dangerously potent masculinity that made her intensely aware that she was a woman.

She dismissed the treacherous thought with a firm thrust of her dimpled chin.

'My friend can only wait fifteen minutes.' She tried to sound tart and crisp, but the words came out husky and defensive.

'Any man who will wait only fifteen minutes for you needs his head read,' the man drawled.

Hot prickles broke out all over her skin. It wasn't the words so much—flirtatious comments of that nature normally left her cold, or brought a derisive curl to her lips—it was the fact that the words had come from the mouth of this suave, self-assured stranger, this stunningly attractive businessman, who had success and privilege written all over him.

What is it with this guy? she pondered in confusion. He just didn't add up. First the way he'd stared so intently at her, when he didn't look the type who would stand and gawp at a woman—any woman, let alone a stranger in a lift. And now here he was making silver-tongued personal remarks, when he didn't strike her as the type who would sink to oily flattery either.

'My friend has a plane to catch,' she informed him curtly. 'He can only wait until twelve-fifteen.' She looked pointedly at her watch, her heart sinking when she saw that it was ten past already.

'Then we'd better try to do something,' the stranger responded easily. He thrust out a hand and she tensed, until she realised that he was reaching past her for the emergency phone mounted on the wall. It was an old-fashioned telephone, its ancient dial lacking numbers.

But there was no need to dial. The moment he snatched it from its hook, a voice answered, 'Emergency lift service.'

He explained their predicament, and after an exchange of words he grimaced and hung up. 'They'll send someone straight away. There are no engineers in this building, apparently. We'll just have to wait until help arrives.'

'Did they say how. . .how long they'd be?' She felt a sinking feeling in her stomach. David would be pacing the floor by now. He was probably already losing patience, thinking she'd stood him up. She had only a few minutes left before he gave up and walked out. For good.

'Let's just say I don't like your chances of making your appointment,' came the ironic reply. 'And I'm afraid you won't be able to call your. . .friend. This phone's directly connected to the lift service downtown, not to this building. Never mind. . . I'm sure he'll forgive you once he hears what held you up. If he doesn't, I'd say he's not worth it.'

His unconcern—and the realisation that she was going to be stuck here in this lift with him for heaven knew how long—brought her emotions, anger uppermost, boiling to the surface.

'I'd thank you not to presume my friend's worth or lack of it,' she flared. 'You know nothing about him!'

He didn't even blink. 'I presume he must be worth something. . .to *you*,' he said silkily, 'or you wouldn't be planning to meet him at Kowalsky's. . . Melbourne's most exclusive and *expensive* antique jewellers.'

She caught her breath as the deadly innuendo sank in. Her enraged silence gave him a chance to slip in a further barb, edged with a cynical dryness.

'You must be mighty keen to get those pretty little hands on whatever glittering bauble your friend has promised you. . .or you wouldn't be in such a lather about him walking out on you.'

She opened her mouth and then snapped it shut, too incensed to speak for a second. Of all the insufferable, arrogant, presumptuous—

He laughed. A sharp, unexpected sound in the confines of the antiquated lift. Her eyes leapt to his, catching the amused glint in his black depths. Amusement. . .but no real softness. More a lethally dangerous gleam, she thought, caught off balance by it.

'You have extremely expressive eyes,' he remarked, the laughter still in his voice, licking through it, lightening its rich, deep resonance. 'You'd like to hit me. Go ahead, if it will make you feel better. I plead guilty. I am all those things you're thinking. But it doesn't mean I'm wrong.'

She nearly did hit him. She was sorely tempted to. But lashing out at him like a virago would only lower her further in his eyes. He didn't think much of women, that was obvious. There was a wealth of cynicism in his voice and in his face. A world-weariness. . .disillusionment too, if she wasn't mistaken. Why cement his low opinion of women by acting in the way he expected her to?

She summoned a soft laugh instead, deliberately turning his laughter back on him. 'I suggest you never take up psychiatry,' she advised him lightly, with the faintest hint of derision. 'You'd be bound to fail.' She widened her gaze in mock dismay. 'You're *not* a psychiatrist, I hope?' she asked, injecting a note of pity into her voice.

Something flickered in the black eyes. The corner of his mouth twitched. His voice, when he answered, held an edge of dry humour. 'I'm relieved to be able to say no, I'm not.'

'Relieved?' she echoed. Secretly, she was relieved too. Relieved that he seemed to have a sense of humour!

'Very much so. And I shall bow to your expert advice,' he promised, 'and decline to take that particular career path in the future.' He paused a moment, then added softly, 'Being a man who doesn't like to fail.'

She could well believe that. He wouldn't have had too many failures in his life, she hazarded. Except maybe. . .with women? Or *a* woman? The one who had made him so jaded and cynical?

'Very wise,' she applauded facetiously. And turned away, biting her lip. Did anyone else in this building realise that one of the lifts was stuck between floors, with people trapped inside?

There was no sound of any activity from above or below. Would the emergency lift people take much longer to arrive? And when they did turn up, how much longer would it take them to fix the problem? What if it was difficult to fix? Dangerous, even? She'd seen movies where trapped people had had to climb out through a lift roof, or where the lift had suddenly dropped dramatically. She shuddered at the thought, her hands trembling on the handbag she was still unconsciously clutching to her chest.

She heard a slight movement and tensed, thinking that her companion, sensing her anxiety, was about to close in on her, offering physical comfort. All her nerve-ends sprang to sharp alert. How would she react if he did. . .if he should put his arm round her and pull her close? She began to tremble anew. . .but not with fear this time. . .with something quite different, a strange, heady excitement.

But he didn't move closer, didn't attempt to touch her. Perhaps at the last minute he'd thought better of it, fearing that if he offered a comforting shoulder she might break down completely and he'd have a hysterical female on his hands. Or maybe he'd remembered, just in time, that they were strangers, and he didn't want her leaping to any wrong conclusions.

Instead, he heaved a deep sigh and muttered through clenched teeth, 'I can't stand confined spaces.' He began to pace restlessly back and forth like a caged tiger, his hands clasped behind him.

She looked at him in surprise, her nervousness forgotten. 'You suffer from claustrophobia?' she asked, her heart stirring in sympathy. She wouldn't have thought he'd be the type of man who would suffer from fears of any kind.

He paused, letting his broad shoulders lift and fall in another heavy sigh. 'Even big, tough guys can have phobias,' he said, his mouth twisting in self-mockery.

She nodded slowly. That was true. Even Indiana Jones, the intrepid hero of *Raiders of the Lost Ark*, had his Achilles' heel—in his case a fear of snakes that turned him to quivering jelly.

'Are you all right?' she asked tentatively. As far as she could tell, he didn't appear to be shaking. Or sweating. Or turning deathly pale. But people showed fear in different ways, she guessed, and this man, with his smooth self-confidence and air of worldly experience, had no doubt learned how to cover up his feelings and any fears he might be suffering underneath.

'Having someone with me helps...' The corner of his mouth curved in a self-deprecating smile. 'Someone calm, who doesn't suffer from the same stupid phobia. You don't, do you?' he asked quickly, his eyes spearing hers.

'No, I don't.' She shook her head, her pulses whirling under the force of his dark gaze. 'Um...maybe if you loosened your tie?' she suggested helpfully.

'Ah. Good idea.' He raised a well-shaped hand and began to wrestle with the knot of his red-patterned silk tie. 'Damn! I feel all thumbs. This wretched knot! I can't seem to—'

'I'll do it,' she said hastily, not wanting him to start panicking. She reached up, her hand brushing his as he drew it back, the brief touch bringing a tingling awareness of rough warmth, of fine hairs on firm skin.

'Thank you.' His lean, strong-jawed face was very close to hers now. She could actually feel the warmth of his breath on her cheek. Her heart began to hammer in a ridiculously wayward fashion. She hadn't been this aware of a man for—

She stepped back abruptly, almost tripping over her own feet, forgetting for a moment that she was wearing high heels. She was so used to wearing sensible flatties during the day.

His hand shot out to steady her.

'You're sure *you're* all right?' he asked, with a quick, amused smile. A smile uptilted at one corner, with more good-humoured charm this time than cynicism.

'I—I'm fine.' She found herself flushing. 'I—I didn't want to crowd you, that's why I. . .' She trailed off with a shrug. 'I'm sure we won't have to wait much longer,' she assured him brightly, darting another quick look at her watch. Twelve-twenty!

She drew in her lips, her heart sinking. Would David already have given up, already be making his way down in the other lift? Or would he decide to wait a bit longer? From memory, his plane wasn't due to leave Tullamarine until around two. But he would have to find a taxi and battle the city traffic to the airport, and then queue up for his seat allocation. David hated being late, feeling rushed. He would want to leave early, to give himself plenty of time.

'It strikes me,' the stranger observed softly, 'that we both need to take our minds off our predicament. I find that talking often helps in situations like this. So. . .why don't you tell me something about yourself? You work here in the city, I take it?'

His dark eyes swept over her stylish cherry-red jacket and matching slim-line skirt, and for a foolish, prickling moment, she was glad she'd dressed up a bit today, knowing she was coming into town, instead of wearing her usual working gear: practical skirt with a shirt or sweater, or tailored trousers as she sometimes did.

'No. I just came into town to meet. . .my friend. I live and work in the suburbs.' Now he'll lose interest, she thought with a tightening of her lips. High-powered city businessmen—and this man looked the epitome of just that—didn't waste their time on people who didn't belong to their fast, slick, self-important world, on insignificant nobodies who spent their lives outside the power-hungry city rat-race.

'Now let me guess,' he said slowly when she didn't enlighten him further. 'You're in. . .public relations?' he hazarded. 'Finance? Marketing?' He paused. 'Am I warm?'

He's judging me by what I'm wearing now, she thought, her lips curving in a derisive smile.

'Stone-cold,' she said. If he wanted to make a game of it, at least it would pass the time. And take his mind off his claustrophobia.

'Well. . .let me see.' He pursed his lips. She found her eyes riveted to his mouth and looked quickly away. 'Legal work, then? Interior design? Banking?'

She shook her head. 'These aren't my usual working clothes,' she admitted. 'I normally wear something a bit more practical and comfortable for the kind of work I do.' Now it should be interesting, she thought, and waited, eyebrows delicately raised.

'Ah.' He fingered his jaw with long fingers, at the same time letting his dark gaze roam down her body, seeming to pause at the swell of her breast, and again at her exposed knees, before continuing down her long legs to her slim, well-shaped ankles. She had the sudden hot, uncomfortable feeling that he was mentally undressing her, divesting her of her clothes, imagining what lay underneath.

'Oh, hell.' He seemed abruptly to tire of his game. 'If we go on like this, I'm going to end up insulting you; I can see that. If I say a model or an actress, you'll turn out to be a brain surgeon or something. You're *not*, are you?'

'Close. But wrong end of the body,' she quipped. 'I treat feet, not brains. I'm a podiatrist.'

His dark eyebrows shot up. 'Well. I never would have picked it in a month of Sundays. I've never met a podiatrist before, never been to one. So...you know all about feet and what's wrong with them, eh? What kind of people come to you mostly? Little old ladies with bunions?'

She gave an ironic half-smile. It was a common misconception. 'We do get a few, but mostly—in our clinic anyway—we see people with sports injuries. Or problems caused by...flat feet.' She looked pointedly down at his well-polished shoes. 'I take it you don't suffer from that problem?'

'Not that I'm aware of.' Amusement flickered in his eyes, revealing that he did have a sense of humour. 'You work at a hospital?'

'I used to, when I first started out. But now I'm in private practice. Not on my own. I'm at a foot clinic in Surrey Hills with two other podiatrists—a married guy with a young family, who owns the clinic, and a good friend of mine, Gaby, who went through uni with me.'

'You like the work?' he pursued. 'Get many people coming in with—um—smelly feet?' His eyes gently mocked her.

She tilted her head at him. 'You clean your teeth before you go to the dentist, don't you? Well, most people wash their feet before coming to see me!'

'Hmm. Good point. You live near the clinic?'

Did he really want to know, she wondered, or was

he simply passing the time? 'Just around the corner, virtually. I share a flat—it's a house, actually—with Gaby, the other podiatrist.'

'Ah.' It wasn't clear just what he meant by that 'ah'. Did he think she might have been living with David? 'And your family? Your parents?'

His eyes were on her face as he asked the question. She flushed faintly under his scrutiny. She had the weirdest feeling that he was waiting intently for her answer. She couldn't imagine why. He couldn't seriously be interested in her or her family, surely?

'My parents are divorced.'

After what she could only describe as a pregnant pause, he said impassively, 'I'm sorry. You still see both of them?'

A fleeting shadow crossed her face. 'When I can. My father still lives here in Melbourne. But he. . .married again a few years ago, so I don't see him as much as I did before.'

'You don't get on with his new wife?'

'I didn't at first,' she admitted. It wasn't that she'd had anything against Beth personally. It was just that another woman had taken her mother's place in her father's life. After all those years! 'My parents were married for twenty-three years,' she heard herself telling him. 'I was twenty when they separated, my brother twenty-two. Neither of us were living at home by then. . . I think our parents were only waiting until we were off their hands.' Her mouth twisted. 'Since then my brother's been married and divorced as well. Fortunately no children were involved.'

The break-up of her parents' marriage and then her brother's, more recently, had made her wary of marriage, cautious of commitment, of rushing into anything permanent before she was completely sure. If her parents' marriage, which she'd always believed to be happy enough, could fail after twenty-three years. . .

'And your mother?'

Again she felt his eyes on her face, and felt the fine hairs at her nape rising in involuntary response. For a stranger, he was showing an unusual interest in her. . . and in what she had to say. She shook off the thought. She had to remember that he was only making conversation to take his mind off being stuck in this lift. The sensation of being trapped could be a real trauma to someone who was claustrophobic. She had to hand it to him. . .he was managing to control his fear admirably. The least she could do was encourage him to keep on talking.

'You live near her?' he prompted before she could speak, as if he really wanted to know.

She frowned faintly. *Why* would he want to know? Why would he care? She took a deep breath. Humour him, she thought. Why not? You'll never see him again, once you're out of this damned lift.

'My mother's moved to Queensland to live. She's sharing a house in Brisbane with a widowed friend.' She felt a faint pang as she said it. Her mother had left Melbourne so suddenly and unexpectedly, not long after she'd started going out with David. Charlotte had insisted that it had nothing to do with Lucy's father and his second wife, who had been married for some time by then. She had sworn that she wished them well, that it was the plight of her old friend that had decided her. Poor Avril had been very lonely since her husband's death, and needed companionship and support, with her only daughter living overseas.

'A *male* widowed friend?' her companion asked with the ghost of a smile. But there seemed to be more cynicism in the smile than humour.

Faintly puzzled—not that it could be anything personal; he didn't even know her mother so it had to be women in general—Lucy lifted her gaze to his and met the probing, magnetic force of his dark eyes. At once a veil seemed to come down over them.

Trembling slightly, from confusion more than anything else, she forced an answer. 'A *woman* friend. An old friend of my mother's. They were at school together, and met up again after they were married.' This man was obviously cynical about all women... that was all it was. What on earth could have happened to him to make him like this?

But the stranger didn't seem interested in her mother's friend. 'And do you get your good looks from your mother...or your father?' he asked, lifting an eyebrow.

She felt an odd little jolt inside. So he thought she was good-looking, did he? An unexpected ripple of pleasure ran through her, though she had a feeling she should have been hearing warning bells instead.

'People say I'm the image of my mother as she used to be when she was my age.' She knew it was true, having seen the likeness in family photograph albums.

'Ah.' He absorbed that for a moment. 'And what else have you inherited from your mother?' he asked, his lip quirking. 'Perhaps you were named after her as well?'

Lucy hid a smile, a quiver flittering through her. So...he was trying to find out her name now, was he? 'My mother's name is Charlotte,' she answered with a shake of her head. 'Mine's Lucy.'

'Ah...Lucy. Pretty name.' Instead of seizing the opportunity to introduce himself, he added musingly, 'I knew a Charlotte once. Only to her family she was always known as Lottie.'

'My mother doesn't like being called Lottie. She prefers Charlotte.' Lucy stole a look up at him. Was he asking all these questions—questions that couldn't possibly be of any real interest to him—to avoid her asking questions of *him*?

'Mmm...well, I can't say I blame her.' The crooked smile flashed briefly. 'So tell me, Lucy...what have you inherited from your father? His temperament, perhaps?'

She drew in her lips, puzzled by some odd inflection

in his voice. Or was it the way he was watching her, his
narrowed eyes piercingly intent on her face? He could
hardly be bowled over by her beauty. . .she wasn't *that*
good-looking!

'I'm not sure I've inherited anything noticeable from
my father at all,' she said a trifle shakily. Her brother
Mike, she mused, was more like her father. In looks
and in temperament. Their father was a decent, amiable, good-natured man. Steady—some might say
stolid—dependable, like a rock. A gentleman even
during the difficult time of his separation from his wife
after twenty-three years of marriage.

Maybe that was why she'd been initially attracted to
David, Lucy reflected, because she'd wanted a steady,
reliable man like her father. Only she was beginning to
realise that wasn't what she really wanted after all.
Something—she wasn't sure what—was missing.

A silence had fallen between them. The stranger
seemed as lost in his own thoughts as she was in hers.
But eventually he asked, 'Was your mother a podiatrist
too? Is that why you took it up?'

'Heavens, no. My mother's expertise lay in another
direction entirely.' Did he grill all the women he met,
even strangers in lifts, about their family backgrounds?
she found herself wondering idly. Was background—
upbringing—*pedigree*—so important to him? Her lip
curled. Judging by the fine cloth of his suit, his soft,
cultured voice and his polished, imperious, almost
arrogantly self-assured manner, his own background
was impeccable. No doubt he'd been brought up to
believe that background—privilege, wealth, success—
meant everything.

Her voice cooled slightly. 'I took on podiatry because
my friend Gaby was studying it. She got me interested,
and I thought. . .why not?'

'Why not, indeed?' If he'd noted any coolness in her
tone he gave no sign of it. His mouth even curved into

a quite devastating smile as he asked, 'And your mother? Where did her expertise lie?'

Her eyes wavered. Though his tone was casual and the impact of his smile would have charmed a snake, there was something... Something that warned her not to be fooled. There's more to all this probing, she thought with a frown, than a snobbish desire to check out a stranger's pedigree...more to all these questions than a claustrophobic's anxiety to keep the conversation rolling, I'll swear it.

And then the answer struck her. 'You *are* a psychiatrist!' she burst out, a flash of turquoise brightening the blue of her eyes. It seemed the only logical explanation. 'You've been secretly laughing at me all along, haven't you? Well, you've finally given yourself away!' she cried in triumph. 'You've been asking too many questions. Shrinks simply can't help themselves. They *have* to ask questions!'

He laughed...a short, sharp sound. To Lucy, it had a slightly hollow ring. 'Oh, you know shrinks well, do you?' His tone, his body language, everything about him—on the surface, at least—was relaxed enough, but she would have sworn that underneath he was irritated for some reason or tense about something. But what? Because she'd steered the conversation in a direction he didn't want?

'I've met a few shrinks in my time,' she informed him, her chin jutting. 'We had a psychiatric unit at the hospital where I used to work. Well, *are* you?' It was about time she turned the tables and started firing a few questions at him for a change. 'If not a psychiatrist...a psychologist?'

'Sorry to disappoint you, but I'm neither...as I told you before. I'm just a boring run-of-the-mill businessman.'

A businessman, she could believe. A wealthy, successful one, she had no doubt. But boring? Run-of-the-mill? Hah!

'What line of business?' she asked, curious despite herself.

Before he had a chance to answer—assuming he'd been going to—the lift jolted and began to move.

'They've fixed it!' she cried unnecessarily. And added, with quick compassion, 'Now you can breathe a bit easier.'

Instead of agreeing with her he responded in a lazy drawl, with a sardonic twist of his lip, 'On the contrary. . .I was just beginning to enjoy myself.'

She shot him a quick look, and glimpsed again the dangerous gleam in his eye that had disturbed her earlier. Heat whipped into her cheeks. 'I'm glad you managed to get your phobia under control,' she said, her tone deliberately dry. She was beginning to wonder if it had ever existed in the first place.

'Mmm. . .with your help.' Was that a *twinkle* in his eye now? 'You must admit it took your mind off your own. . .anxieties,' he said smoothly as the lift came to a crunching halt at the sixth floor.

She gaped at him. Was he *admitting* he'd faked his phobia? She felt a stab of pique at being made a fool of, then stifled it, realising he had only done it to calm *her*, to give her something else to think about. Good psychology!

'I take it all back,' she said with a quick, contrite smile. 'I think you might have made a good psychologist after all.'

'You have a delightful smile.' His eyes were on her mouth. 'I thought you would.'

She looked away quickly, and immediately regretted it, feeling like kicking herself for reacting like a bashful schoolgirl. Why hadn't she simply accepted the compliment, been gracious about it, and then dismissed it from her mind as she would have done with anyone else? What was it about this man that made her feel so. . .?What *was* it she felt? Vulnerable? Confused? Off-balance? All of those!

And then she remembered David. She hadn't given him a thought, she realised contritely, for some time. Would he still be up here waiting for her?

She sighed. Highly unlikely! Not after all this time. He'd warned her... And this time, she knew, he'd meant it. By now he was probably already at the airport, or even boarding his plane right this minute, thinking she'd stood him up deliberately.

She swore under her breath as the heavy lift doors jerked open.

CHAPTER TWO

THEY had to announce themselves and wait to be inspected through a small glass aperture before the door to Kowalsky's opened. Lucy was bristlingly aware of the dark stranger close behind her as she stepped inside.

It was more like a cluttered workroom than a display room, though there were glass display cases in evidence. Two men, one young, the other middle-aged, were bent over work benches, doing repair work or creating new pieces in the antique style for which Kowalsky was famous. A third man, an elderly, grey-haired man wearing thick bifocals, emerged from behind a large desk. There was no sign of David.

'Mr Travers!' The old man looked straight past her, his rather myopic gaze lighting up at the sight of the man behind her. 'Good to see you again. Please... come in.' Obviously Mr Travers was a good customer here. Seeking valuable baubles for his wife? Or his mistress? Or, if he wasn't married, for one of his *women*? He didn't look the kind of man who would be without a woman in his life. More likely a *succession* of women, judging by the cynical lines round his mouth.

'I'm Joe Kowalsky.' The old man finally turned to her, obviously thinking that she was with Mr Travers. Thinking she was one of his women, no doubt. A valuable customer-to-be. I guess I ought to feel flattered, Lucy mused with a wry twitch of her lip.

'We're not together,' she said quickly. 'My name is Lucy Farrell. I was to meet a friend of mine here. David Mortimer. But the lift got stuck and—' She let her hand flutter in the air. 'Has he gone, do you know?'

'Oh, dear, I'm afraid so. He waited as long as he

25

could, then said he had to go. He seemed convinced that you weren't coming.' The jeweller smiled sympathetically. 'You must have taken the lift we've been having trouble with lately. I think it needs a complete overhaul. I'd avoid that one going down, if I were you.'

He squinted past her at the man standing silently behind. 'Do have a look around, Mr Travers,' he invited. 'We have quite a few new pieces on display.' It was plain he wasn't about to let a valuable client like Mr Travers slip through his fingers. Plain too that he'd already dismissed Lucy as a potential client. Her man had gone.

But politeness forced him to turn back to her to ask, 'Is there anything I can help you with, Miss Farrell?'

'No...thank you, Mr Kowalsky.' She backed away. 'I'll be on my way. I'll take the other lift down...as you suggest.' She swung round, intending to slip past her companion of the past half-hour with no more than a brief nod.

'Hey...wait. I'll come with you.' Mr Travers paused only long enough to throw a last word in Joe Kowalsky's direction, 'I'll come back later, Joe,' before extending an arm and sweeping Lucy out through the door.

As it shut behind them she turned to face him, aware of a wild fluttering in her chest, a rosy warmth in her cheeks.

'There's no need to see me down. I'll be all right.' She heard the faint breathlessness in her voice and tried to steady it. 'I'll just make sure I take the other lift this time.'

'Maybe I want you to see *me* down,' he said, his mouth curving into a grin that on any other man would have been sheepish, but on this man seemed more droll than self-effacing.

She eyed him uncertainly. Maybe his phobia about lifts really did exist after all and he was trying to hide how bad it was. But was it really so bad that he wouldn't step into a lift by himself? She *had* come across people like that, who avoided travelling alone in a lift. But this man. . .he appeared so coolly self-possessed, so strong-minded. Not the type to give in to a phobia. . .or to any kind of fear for that matter. No, he'd simply dreamed up his phobia to put *her* at ease. . . to prevent her dissolving into hysterics. She'd be crazy to fall for it again.

Unless. . .her stomach rolled over. . .unless it had just been an excuse to chat her up?

Dream on, Lucy, she told herself. Suave, high-flying city business types like this man—obviously well-known and successful too, judging by the way Joe Kowalsky had deferred to him—chose smooth, sophisticated women to match. They didn't go around chasing after sports-mad suburban working girls. *And* he was probably married. 'Never get involved with a married man.' Charlotte had drummed that into her for as long as Lucy could remember. 'They'll use you. . .make all the promises in the world. . .and then dump you without turning a hair.'

As they waited for the lift her companion asked curiously, 'Did you say *David* Mortimer?'

Startled, she glanced up at him. Surely he couldn't know David? 'That's right.'

'The David Mortimer who works for Maxi Board?' There was a whimsical glint in his eye.

'Yes!' Her surprise was evident in her voice. 'You know him?' She wasn't sure why she should be so surprised. David worked for a large, well-known company. It wasn't so impossible that the two could have met somewhere. It was just that they seemed so. . . different. Worlds apart, she would have thought. David, the stolid, modest-living engineer who liked tinkering with old cars. And this man, so polished and urbane, the epitome of the jet-setting, super-successful city businessman.

The corner of his mouth slanted upwards. 'He works for me.'

Now she did gape. 'Works for you?' she echoed stupidly.

'Well, not directly under me. He's an engineer at one of my plants—Maxi Board's corrugated box plant at Oakleigh. It's part of the Travers group of companies.'

Her jaw sagged. *Travers!* Oh, hell. Why on earth hadn't she connected the name? 'You're *Case* Travers?' David's big boss!

'Correct.'

She flicked her tongue over her lips, her mind casting back. Case Travers. . .the golden boy, as David had once referred to him. The lucky only son, who had recently taken over control of Maxi Board and the entire Travers group of packaging and paperboard companies following the tragic death of his father, Nicholas Travers, Maxi Board's founder. David had told her all about it, and she'd read about the tragedy in the papers. Nicholas Travers and his wife Sophie had both been killed instantly when their Lear jet had come down in a violent storm over the Warrumbungle Ranges.

'I'm sorry. . . I—I had no idea who you were,' she faltered. 'I. . . It must have been shocking for you. . . losing both your parents like that.'

Nicholas and Sophie Travers had been happily married, she recalled David telling her, for more than forty years. Which, for a workaholic like Nicholas Travers, who'd been away from home so much, building up his business empire, had struck her as pretty amazing. To be happily married for so long. . . It had almost brought tears to her eyes, tears of regret that her own parents' marriage hadn't been happier, hadn't lasted the distance. She had never dreamed, right up until the day her mother and father had agreed to separate, that their marriage would ever fall apart.

'Thank you. . .that's kind of you.' Case Travers nodded briefly. 'After you,' he said as their lift arrived.

'Let's keep our fingers crossed, shall we?' He tossed
her a wink as they stepped in.

She gave a quick smile, still slightly stunned by the
revelation that he was David's *el supremo*—Maxi
Board's big boss. Despite David's snide comments
about sons with silver spoons in their mouths, he'd
conceded that Case Travers had a brilliant mind, and
impressive qualifications for the massive empire he'd
inherited. He'd starred at university, then later amassed
further qualifications and business experience overseas,
before working his way up from the lowliest position in
the family business until he was familiar with all aspects
of the various Travers companies.

But—she eyed him critically—it was still inherited
wealth. An inherited multinational business empire.
He'd hardly started from nothing, or built up the
business from scratch by his own endeavours. He'd
probably been spoilt rotten all his life, had had everything he'd ever wanted. And he was probably insuffer-
ably selfish and conceited as a result—under that sexy,
charismatic, ravishingly charming façade.

'So it was David you were to meet here today,' Case
remarked on the way down. 'What was the occasion?
It's not your birthday, is it?'

'No. . .nothing like that. He. . .' She hesitated, wary
about opening up to this man, of all men. David's big
boss!

'Go on, I won't bite. He. . .what?'

She took a deep breath. 'He wanted to buy me an
engagement ring,' she admitted in a rush.

'Ah. . .' Case Travers nodded slowly. 'No wonder
you were so anxious to get to your appointment on
time.' He eyed her for a long, speculative moment, his
black eyes boring into her guarded blue ones, as if they
were seeing more than she wanted to reveal. 'Or. . .
were you?'

'What do you mean?' she breathed, her palms feeling
suddenly moist.

'You were running late, if I recall. It was already past twelve before you stepped into the lift, and you told me you were supposed to be meeting him at midday and that he was only going to wait until twelve-fifteen at the very latest. It strikes me that maybe you were dragging your feet because you *wanted* something to delay you. Now, why would that be, I wonder? Because. . .' he stroked his strongly carved jaw '. . .you aren't altogether sure how you feel about him?'

'Oh, that's ridiculous!' she cried. But *was* it? She forced up her chin. 'If that lift hadn't got stuck I would have got there before David left.'

'Maybe,' he conceded drily, but the dark glitter in his eyes showed he didn't believe it. 'Well, don't worry, Lucy. . .I may call you Lucy, I trust? And, please, David calls me Case—all my engineers do. You must too.' He pursed his well-shaped lips. 'He'll ask you again, won't he?'

His tone was sardonic now, the cynical lines round his mouth appearing more marked. As if he was used to female games, and thought she had been playing one with David, deliberately playing hard to get. Did he think she was holding out for a bigger and better diamond ring? Was *that* it?

She buried her indignation, and said with a sigh, 'That's just it. He won't.' She hesitated, then admitted, 'That's why I had to meet him on time. He said if I didn't arrive by twelve-fifteen at the very latest he'd know my answer was no. And he wouldn't be asking me again.'

Case raised a dark eyebrow. 'So. . .he'd given you an ultimatum, had he?' He spoke in a lazy drawl, his eyes narrowing. 'And yet you were cutting it so fine that even if that lift hadn't broken down you would have been lucky to have made it.' He searched her face for a long moment, then asked curiously, 'Was it his ultimatum you were rebelling against, Lucy? Or was it that you really *are* unsure. . .about whether to say yes at all?'

She flushed scarlet. 'Neither!' she cried, and wondered at the same time, with a stab of unease, if she
was protesting too much, if that *was* the real reason
she'd been running late.

But she was hardly going to admit it to David's boss!
'I wasn't fighting against anything... I was just running
late,' she asserted. 'People *do* run late, you know.
When they lead busy lives,' she added pointedly.

He obviously had all the spare time in the world.
Time to visit antique jewellers in the middle of the day.
Time to change his mind glibly and declare he'd be
back later. Time to chat up strange women. But then,
he was the big boss. He could do as he liked. It was the
people who worked *for* him who were on the tight
schedule, who worked hard for a living. People like
David.

'Not so busy that they have to miss lunch though...
surely?' came the smooth response.

She glanced up at him quickly. Uncertainly. Surely
he couldn't mean—?

'I'll buy a sandwich on my way back to work,' she
decided hastily.

'You're working this afternoon?' he asked, waving
her out of the lift as it reached ground level.

'Of course. Why? Aren't you?' she asked mockingly
as she stepped out into the tiled lobby.

He ignored the question. 'What time do your afternoon appointments start?' She felt his hand at her
elbow, felt his presence close behind her as they crossed
the lobby to the open doorway leading onto Collins
Street.

'Three o'clock,' she admitted after a slight pause.
Normally she had appointments from two o'clock, but
today she'd put them back in case David had wanted
her to drive him to the airport.

Her lip curled ruefully at the thought. For once he'd
meant what he'd said. He hadn't waited a moment
longer than he'd vowed he would. Did he think that

tactic would make her come to heel the next time he
asked her to marry him? Or had he meant it when he'd
vowed it would be over, finished, if she didn't turn up?

'Good. Then I'll take you to lunch. The Regent's
closest. They're bound to have a spare table.'

She felt a bristle of resentment at the high-handed
way he was assuming she would simply fall in with his
plans. For Case Travers, she mused sourly, any top
restaurant in Melbourne, no doubt, would have a table
ready and waiting, any time he asked.

She tossed her head, her silky hair swinging, softly
caressing her long neck. 'There's no need—'

'I think there is. It's the least I can do to make up for
your. . .disappointment today.' She caught the slight
hesitation before the word 'disappointment', and the
faint mockery in his voice as he said it.

Damn, she cursed silently. I've said too much. David
won't relish his big boss knowing his personal problems. I should have shut up. . .or at least covered up
better.

'Why should you have to make anything up to me?'
she demanded tartly. 'You weren't the one who made
the lift break down.'

'True. But your. . .friend David works for me. And I
may be in a position to put things right for you and
give you another chance with him.' He raised a taunting
eyebrow. 'If you want another chance?'

Her chin came up. 'I can manage my own personal
affairs, thank you. But. . .I appreciate your concern,'
she added, realising how rude the retort must have
sounded.

He gave a brief chuckle. Obviously he was thick-
skinned enough to take it. He was probably used to
dealing with abuse—and shrugging it off—in his high-
powered, cut-throat business dealings. 'Nevertheless,'
he said coolly, 'let's have a bite of lunch together. I
think we deserve a bit of relaxation after our shared
trauma, don't you?'

She was about to refuse when she thought, Why not? It wasn't every day she had an invitation to the Regent for lunch. And he *was* David's boss. 'I guess so.' She gave in with a smile. She didn't feel so sure, though, that she was going to find it relaxing. There was something about this man that made her feel anything *but* relaxed.

As it happened, there were plenty of tables available at the restaurant he took her to, the luxurious Le Resturant, high up in the Regent Hotel. When they had been shown to a window table, with stunning views over the city and parklands, Case said, 'Take a look at the view for a moment, Lucy, while I slip out and make a couple of phone calls. Be right back.'

'Fine,' she said, thankful that he hadn't produced a mobile phone and proceeded to use it at the table as she'd seen some businessmen do. 'In fact. . .' she edged away from the table herself '. . .I'll just pop into the powder room and freshen up a bit while you're making your calls.'

As they headed off, she in one direction, he in the other, she wondered idly who he was calling. His secretary? His wife? Was he the type of man who would be open and honest with his wife about taking another woman out to lunch, or would he keep quiet about it?Did he *have* a wife, for that matter? Or was he a free agent, on the look-out, perhaps, for a new woman in his life? She vaguely recalled David mentioning that his new chief was rarely seen out of business hours without a beautiful woman on his arm, but whether he'd meant a wife or a succession of women. . . Why hadn't she taken more notice?

Her heart fluttered at the thought of this man—this sexy, attractive hunk—being on the look-out for a woman. Fool! she instantly berated herself. Men like Case Travers didn't have to go *looking* for a woman. Women undoubtedly came swarming from all sides. He could take his pick—his pick of the cream of

Melbourne society, if that was his taste. Which, with his staggeringly wealthy, powerful background, was more than likely.

Before returning to her table, she paused at the mirror in the glamorous powder room to gaze for a bemused moment at her reflection. . .at the face that seemed to have caught *his* eye for some reason. Nothing too remarkable about it, really. He must know far more beautiful and elegant women he could have invited to lunch. Why was he going out of his way to spend his time with her when he didn't have to? She'd be a fool to kid herself that it was because he was in any way attracted to her. If they hadn't got stuck in that lift together, he wouldn't have looked at her twice.

And yet. . .he *had* looked at her twice. She'd caught him looking at her before they'd even stepped into the lift.

Maybe she'd just imagined it, turned a glance of normal curiosity into something more. It wasn't as if there'd been anyone else for him to look at.

Since then, of course, events had rather thrown them together. But, still, he hadn't *had* to invite her to lunch. . .

Was it because of David? Because David was a valued Maxi Board employee? Was Case Travers the kind of employer who would feel an obligation towards his employees, particularly one of his senior engineers?

She shrugged, and swung away. Maybe, over lunch, she would find out.

Case was already back at the table, consulting the wine list. 'French chablis suit you?' he asked, half rising as she joined him.

'Fine.' She was surprised he'd even bothered to ask.

Over their Caesar salads and delicately cooked Atlantic salmon they talked of various things. Inconsequential things to begin with, like the sculpture exhibition at the Arts Centre, the beautifully restored Regent Theatre, and the thriving Southbank development along the Yarra River, which at night, they both agreed, with the reflections in the river and the old buildings enhanced by amber lighting, could be Paris or anywhere in Europe. Then more personal matters crept in.

'Your mother lives in Brisbane, you said?' His eyes met hers fleetingly. 'North or south of the river?'

Her eyes flickered under his gaze. Why would he want to know that? Why would he care? 'North. Towards the airport,' she told him diffidently. 'Why?' she blurted.

He quirked a lip, brushing the question aside. 'I guess you miss her. . .living so far away?'

'Well, yes. . .I do miss her,' she admitted, and paused. His eyes encouraged her to go on, so she did, though she was sure she'd see his eyes glaze over with boredom at any second. 'And I think she misses both of us too— my brother and I. But she says we don't need her as much as Avril does right now. And my mother's entitled to live her own life.'

She shrugged, surprised to see that his eyes were still as sharp and intent as ever. She heard herself babbling on. 'My brother and I are always pretty busy, what with one thing and another. Mike—my brother—is a company secretary. And a mad-keen golfer. He loves his footy too. . .'

'And what else do *you* like to do, when you're not treating people's feet?' Case asked as she trailed off. He was giving her his full attention still, as if he really wanted to know.

She would have given much to know what thoughts lay behind the fathomless black eyes. . .what circumstances in his life had etched the hard, cynical lines in his face. Was it everything having come too easily to him making him jaded with life and people? Then why did he seem so riveted by *her* mundane ramblings?

'I compete in triathlons,' she told him, and saw his brow shoot up. 'I train a fair bit, especially during the season—which has finished for now until after winter. Even in winter I try to go for a swim every morning, at a public pool. And I go bike-riding. I run. I go to the gym. And, since you ask—' for whatever reason, she thought '—I like movies and plays, and when I have the chance,' she added, her eyes twinkling defiance, 'I like to go to the footy too.' Case Travers would be used to his lunch companions having more sophisticated, feminine interests, no doubt. 'I'm a one-eyed Demon fan,' she told him, 'like my father and brother.'

'Well, what do you know? A Demon fan. Melbourne's my team too.'

'Really?' she said politely. But I bet you don't sit in the open stands in the wet and the cold like we do, Lucy thought. I bet it's a corporate box or the members' stand for you.

'Triathlons, eh?' He rolled the word round on his tongue. Feigning interest? 'That entails. . .swimming, cycling and running, doesn't it? Sounds strenuous.'

'I do it for fun,' she asserted. Believe it or not, Case Travers, she added silently. 'I enjoy it.' She was about to ask what he did for relaxation, but he slipped in another question first.

'And David? He shares your sporting interests?'

She shrugged, her lashes sweeping down. 'Not really.' She wished he hadn't reminded her of David. It made her feel guilty. As well as confused and unsure about her future. Would David be relieved when he found out that she hadn't deliberately stood him up? Would he welcome her back into his life with open arms? Did she really *want* him to?

She blinked in shock, and felt a stab of self-reproach that the question had even surfaced. Of *course* she did! She'd be mad not to. David was a good man. He'd make a wonderful husband and a wonderful father and he would always be there, steady as a rock, to rely on. If she'd been getting cold feet lately, it was nothing *he'd* done. . .it was. . .it was her mother's fault. The way

Charlotte kept urging her to be sure. . .to be sure. . .to be sure. . . Until she wanted to throw up her hands and forget the whole thing.

'He doesn't?' Case prompted, and she blinked again, realising he was waiting for elaboration.

'Well. . .' She might as well be frank. 'Sport's not really his thing. Except for going to the footie with me sometimes, when I manage to get there myself. Not that he's madly keen. He only comes along for my sake. He'd rather be working on his cars. Restoring old cars is his hobby. He and his father are restoring a vintage Delage at present.'

'Doesn't sound as if you see too much of him.'

'Well, we don't live in each other's pockets,' she conceded. 'But there's usually some spare time at the weekends to get together. Or odd nights during the week.'

'But not this week,' he drawled. 'He's gone away, you say. On business?'

'He's gone to a conference. There's a big pulp and paper conference in Surfers Paradise this week.'

'Ah. . .that. Yes, of course. I recall seeing his name on the list of delegates.' At her surprised look, he added with a sardonic smile, 'David doesn't need my permission. He reports to his plant manager or to my general manager, John Castle—my brother-in-law.' He raised his glass languidly and took a long sip of his wine. 'I happen to be going to the conference myself the day after tomorrow. . .just for the last day.'

Lucy's eyelashes flickered as she glanced up at him quickly. Did that mean he would see David? He'd be bound to!'

'Do you suppose—' she swallowed '—you'll have a chance to speak to David while you're there?' David was, after all, one of Maxi Board's senior engineers. He was even giving a paper at the conference.

'I'll be making sure I speak to all my Maxi Board people.'

She moistened her lips with a quick sip of wine. 'Will you. . .will you mention to him that I got stuck in that lift with you on my way up to meet him?' Would he bother? No doubt he had better things to do on his only day at the conference than arrange a private conversation with one of his engineers on an errant girlfriend's behalf.

'I have a better idea,' Case murmured. 'I think he'd rather you tell him yourself.'

She flushed. Just as she'd thought. He had more important things to bother about in his limited time there. 'I—I will. Naturally. When he gets back—'

'That's not what I meant,' he slid in smoothly.

'What—what do you mean? That I should try to ring him? At the conference?'

'I was thinking of a more personal approach. Face to face.' He eyed her coolly. 'Why don't you fly up with me on Friday and stay at Surfers for a couple of days? I have a spare plane ticket. You could patch things up with David and then visit your mother in Brisbane at the weekend. It's only a short drive from Surfers.'

She gaped at him. He had it all worked out! Was this how he was used to operating? Making spur-of-the-moment decisions affecting other people, even people he barely knew, confident that they'd fall in with his plans. . .as she'd fallen in with his plans for lunch?

'That—that's crazy!' she spluttered. 'I can't just—'

'Why not?' He sat back indolently, his expression gently mocking. 'Can't you postpone your appointments for one day? Hand over any urgent cases to one of your colleagues?'

'No!' she cried, even as her mind leapt at the prospect.

'You're saying no before you've even thought it over. Look, you'll have one and a bit days to organise things before we go. One weekday off isn't so difficult to arrange, is it? And with the weekend to follow you could have virtually three days in Queensland. You'll

have time to see David and patch things up with him,
time to visit your mother, even time to enjoy some
tropical sunshine. There won't be any expense. Maxi
Board will cover all that. We've a block booking at the
conference hotel. I'll handle all that.'

He was making her head reel. 'I couldn't let you—'

'But I insist. I find it's in my own interests to keep
my employees and their. . .loved ones happy. Why are
you hesitating?' His eyes impaled hers. 'You do want
to be reunited with David, don't you? Or. . .*do* you?'

'Yes, of course I—' She broke off, then cried, 'But
not like this! I—I feel I'm being—' She was about to
say 'manipulated', but recalled, just in time, that he was
David's boss.

'Steamrollered?' Case suggested, amused irony in his
voice.

She felt a rush of heat to her cheeks. 'I'm sorry to
sound ungrateful, but. . .' She trailed off with a flutter
of her hands.

'But you don't like feeling steamrollered.' There was
a grudging respect in his voice. And maybe a trace of
surprise. 'You felt your friend David was steamrollering you too, by giving you that ultimatum, didn't you?
Well, I certainly don't wish you to feel steamrollered,
Lucy. . .or manipulated,' he added with the ghost of a
smile, as if he'd known all along that that was what
she'd been thinking. 'But I would like you to think
about it.'

The black eyes were steady on hers. . .compelling in
their intensity. She found it impossible to look away.

'I—I don't have anything suitable to wear,' she
argued, and realised, with horror, that she was weakening. . .teetering on the edge of giving in.

A sceptical eyebrow shot up. 'I can't believe that. A
sporty, outdoor girl like you. Not that I'd bother too
much, if I were you. There are boutiques full of
glamorous resort-wear at Surfers. Buy what you need
when you get there. You might like to pack an evening

dress, though...there's a dinner dance the night we arrive. I'm sure David will want you to be there.'

Lucy's mind whirled, temptation warring with a flash of resentment at his high-handed assumption that everyone had the time and the money to buy whatever their heart desired.

It was obvious that he was a man used to giving orders and making snap decisions—with money no object—and having people fall in with whatever he decided. As head of a giant enterprise like the one he now controlled, she guessed he'd have to be decisive. But that didn't give him the right...

'And will your...wife be flying up with us?' she asked, eyeing him ingenuously. 'To be with you at the dinner dance?'

There was an electric pause. She saw his mouth twist into a smile that was more derisive than amused.

'You obviously don't know too much about me,' he said curtly. 'I happen to be divorced.'

Divorced! For some odd reason that surprised her. And...disappointed her? Why was it that nobody could stay married any more? Not her parents, not her brother, not even this stunningly successful, dynamic man. Did nobody these days take marriage seriously? There were odd exceptions, of course, like Case Travers' own parents, who'd stayed happily married, by all reports, for forty-odd years. But they were a rarity, sadly.

'You disapprove,' he said, his tone sardonic.

'Don't be silly,' she denied quickly. 'My own brother's divorced. And my parents. I know it... happens. It happens all the time. Were you married for long?' she couldn't resist asking.

'Two years.' He sounded terse now, his eyes on his wine glass, not on her. It was obvious he didn't want to talk about it.

But some perverse imp of curiosity drove her on. 'Do you have any children?'

'No children.' His eyes lifted, chilly now as they met hers. He seemed annoyed that she wasn't taking the hint. 'Mercifully, we didn't have that complication,' he said tonelessly.

She steeled herself not to blink under his cold gaze, or look away. 'You asked *me* some rather personal questions,' she reminded him. 'Yet you won't allow me the same right?'

He heaved a sigh, his eyes losing some of their cold glitter, his expression resigned now. But his tone, when he spoke, was still cool, tinged now with irony. 'What do you want to know? Why my wife left me?'

His wife had left *him*? It hadn't been a mutual decision, then? She found it hard to believe that any woman would willingly walk out of a marriage to this man...this ravishingly attractive, magnetic dynamo. But she didn't know him, of course. Maybe, in private, he was a monster. Or maybe he'd played around. That was more like it. Her lip twisted. He had the looks, the money, the power, the charisma to chase after any woman he wanted or lusted after. The realisation brought with it a swift qualm. And here she was, agreeing to fly up north with him...

'I take it, by that curl of your lip, that you're imagining all kinds of lurid things about me,' he taunted softly, his glittering eyes causing a wave of heat to rise up her throat. 'Let me put your mind at ease. My wife, far from seeing me as a philandering Lothario or a physical threat, accused me of being dull and boring.'

Dull and boring? *This* man? She stared at him, her heart inexplicably lightening all of a sudden. She let her tight lips relax, ignoring the quiver deep down inside her which was warning her that nothing about this man was safe, let alone dull and boring.

'And are you?' she heard herself asking him.

He flashed a smile...a self-deprecating but breathtakingly attractive smile. 'I'm not a wildly social animal. She is.'

He wasn't? She found that hard to believe too. A man of his background and exalted position in life? She cast a look up at him from under her lashes, imagining him in a social context, at ease, in command of himself and those around him, the focus of all eyes. Female eyes in particular. If he wasn't a social animal it couldn't be due to any lack of social skills, or any lack of charm or appeal.

'She's happy now, by all accounts.' He traced the rim of his glass with an idle finger. 'She's remarried. Someone more to her taste. A diplomat based in Paris. Endless parties. The chance to dress up and socialise every night. She's in her element.'

The cynical undertone was back in his voice. And now she knew what lay behind it. His wife—undoubtedly a raving beauty, with the charm and social graces to bewitch any man she chose, Case included—had turned out to be a shallow, spoilt, grasping, discontented bitch, by the sound of it. Presumably unfaithful as well. The experience, understandably, had scarred him, soured him. She felt swift compassion, and made an attempt to lighten the conversation.

'Well, I'm glad to hear you're going to be social-minded enough to go to this dinner dance at Surfers on Friday night.' She injected a gently teasing note into her voice. 'If I do fly up with you, and David wants me to go to the dinner with him, I'll expect you to keep a dance for me,' she heard herself declaring recklessly.

'That's a promise.' A glint of humour lightened the inky black depths of his eyes. 'I'll try not to step on your toes. Mustn't have our trusty podiatrist suffering from sore feet.'

'I'll bet you're a superb dancer,' she said with a shaky laugh, glad to see that his sense of humour hadn't deserted him along with his wife. And then a sickening thought struck her. 'You're not flying up in a small plane, are you?' If *she* had any phobia, it was small planes. If he was, it would make her decision easy.

'No.' The trace of humour vanished in an instant, an icy film coming down over his eyes. 'I decided not to replace our company jet after it. . .crashed. All our company executives take commercial flights these days. A private jet is an unnecessary extravagance anyway, in my book.'

Her face flamed in mortification as she recalled the plane crash which had killed his parents. 'Case, I'm sorry. . .I didn't think.'

'It was a perfectly reasonable question,' he said dismissively, the harsh lines round his mouth easing a trifle. 'So. . .you'll try to arrange things so that you can fly up with me on Friday morning?'

He was covering his grief well, but it was there. . . She could sense it, feel it. She felt another quick surge of compassion for him. And it was that, more than anything else, that decided her. In that moment she didn't want to disappoint him by throwing his offer back in his face.

'I'll. . .see if I can arrange it.'

'Good.' He leaned back, a satisfied smile on his lips. Seeing it, she felt a belated qualm. She had been so intent on feeling sorry for him that she had forgotten that this was a jaded, cynical, hardened man of the world. A diabolically clever man. And quite ruthless, she realised in the same moment. Ruthless in getting what he wanted. . .in manipulating people. . .imposing his will. Why was she letting him get away with it?

Because he was David's big boss? Or because, deep down, she *wanted* to go? She did want to go, she realised with a trembling sigh. But she preferred not to delve too deeply into her reasons.

'Look. . .why don't you surprise David?' Case suggested, raising his glass to his lips and taking a leisurely sip of the fine wine he'd chosen. 'And surprise your mother as well? No need to let either of them know you're coming, is there? Why not give them both a delightful surprise?'

She tilted her head at him. The idea of playing Cupid amused him, did it? And the thought of being there to witness her springing this surprise visit on David? She felt a prickle of defiance. This was just an amusing, diverting little game to him. Or was it a demonstration of his power—a power game—to show her what a man in his position was capable of?

Why should she humour him?

On the other hand, it probably *was* the sensible thing to do. . .to arrive unannounced. If she tried to ring David in advance he might hang up on her before she had a chance to explain.

'Well. . .I'll see,' she said non-committally. David probably *would* be delighted if she surprised him. But not her mother. Charlotte hated surprises. She always liked to know what was happening in advance. And, since she lived with someone else, it would only be right to let them know she was coming. But she could wait until she was up in Queensland and ring from Surfers. The phone call to Brisbane would be cheaper from there, and she could chat for longer.

'I really ought to be getting back to work,' she said, checking her watch. The time had flown. It occurred to her that she still knew very little about him. She didn't even know if he was currently involved with anyone.

She brushed the thought aside, annoyed with herself for even toying with the question. It was pretty irrelevant anyway. The man was trying to reunite her with David. . .not pursuing her for any clandestine purpose of his own!

CHAPTER THREE

SHE couldn't believe she was actually on her way, sitting beside Case Travers in the first class section of a Boeing 737, heading for Coolangatta. Her mother wouldn't believe it either. Charlotte's quiet, sensible daughter wasn't known for wild, spur-of-the-moment escapades. Even Gaby, good friend that she was, had been stunned but supportive, promising to cover for her in her absence.

'You haven't heard from David?' Case asked over a delectable lunch that Lucy wouldn't have believed possible on a commercial inter-state aircraft.

Her stomach swooped. 'Not a word.' David had obviously meant what he'd said. As far as he was concerned, it was over.

Was he feeling heartbroken about it? Or just a tiny bit relieved? It must have been frustrating for him, she reflected uncomfortably, the way she'd kept putting off making that final commitment. Maybe he was even *happy* to be free. Because now he could get on with his life and maybe in time meet someone else, someone who would love him the way he'd always wanted to be loved. . .unreservedly. Someone who wouldn't blow hot and cold.

And here she was, about to burst back into his life. About to surprise him, expecting him to welcome her back with open arms. And he probably would! Only. . .

She stifled a groan. Had anything really changed? Was she any surer now that she knew she'd come so close to losing him?

'I think I'm making a big mistake!' she blurted out.

Case turned indolently in his plush seat. 'You're saying you don't *want* to see David? Don't *want* to

45

make up with him?' The black eyes, dark glinting slits
under his lowered lids, were impossible to read. Was
he angry that he'd wasted his time and money on her?
Or gratified that he had proved to her, finally, that she
didn't really care for David. . .or not enough? Or was
that contempt in his eyes, a cynical belief that yet
another woman had disappointed him in some way?
She simply couldn't tell. He hid his feelings too well.

'I—I think it's a mistake to surprise him,' she said
lamely, not wanting to admit to her real doubts.
Anyway, what was the point? It was too late to turn
back now.

Case surprised her by reaching for her hand, closing
his fingers over it so that she could feel their warm
strength, their grainy texture—surprisingly work-hard-
ened hands for a man who'd supposedly had everything
handed to him on a platter. She found herself trembling, and desperately hoped that he couldn't feel it.

'I disagree,' he murmured. 'Trust me, Lucy. You're
doing the right thing by flying up and clearing the air
face to face, rather than over the phone or through a
third party. And surprising him will be the icing on the
cake.'

'I guess so,' she said, trying to feel convinced. 'Trust
me,' he'd said. *Could* she trust him? Why did she have
the prickly feeling there was more to his apparent
generosity than he was telling her?

'You haven't let your mother know you're coming
either?' he asked, and she wondered if the change of
subject was to take her mind off David.

'No. . .I haven't,' she said, adding silently, Not yet.
She would, though, as soon as she'd checked in.

She wondered with a flutter if Case would assume
that she'd want to share David's hotel room. No. . .
surely not. Not with all those other paper industry
people there. She wasn't engaged to David. They
weren't even living together. She'd never even spent a
whole night at his flat, although he'd once or twice

stayed at hers, when Gaby had been away for the night—for her protection and comfort, as David had put it at the time. David always had sound reasons for doing the things he did. He never acted on impulse, was never swept into anything by emotion alone. The way she was being swept now...by agreeing to this mad idea.

The thought brought more flutters. Was she, by flying halfway across Australia to see David, also telling him that she was saying yes, she *would* marry him?

'Why the groan?' Case asked, and she realised in dismay that she must have groaned aloud.

'I. . .' She heaved a sigh, not knowing what to say.

'You've got cold feet, haven't you?'

Startled, she snatched back her hand. Case Travers was far too perceptive. 'C-cold feet?' she echoed.

'I was right the other day, wasn't I?' His eyes challenged her to deny it. 'You were late for your appointment with David because deep down you didn't *want* to meet him. You weren't ready to commit yourself to him. I doubt if you ever will be.'

She caught her breath. 'If you believe that,' she shot back, not able to deny it, 'why are you going to so much trouble and expense to throw us back together?'

His mouth curved in an almost diabolical way. Speechless for a second, she could only stare at him. He couldn't mean. . . She felt her mouth go dry, a pulse beating frantically at her temple. Surely, she thought wildly, he hasn't gone to all these lengths to throw *us* together, him and me?

After a chaotic moment, she found her voice. 'Wh-what does that look mean?' she demanded shakily, certain she must be mistaken. It was crazy! Ruthless he might be. . .manipulative. . .and power-mad. . . But to use his power and his money to chase after *her*. . .she needed her head read!

Or did she? Suspicion flared in her eyes. Even royal princes had been known to dally with village girls or housemaids to slake their lascivious appetites and relieve their boredom.

Case was smiling broadly now. An open, genuinely amused smile that gave his face a whole new dimension, easing for a moment the hard, cynical lines that gouged his cheeks. A devastatingly attractive smile that made her wonder if she'd just imagined that devilish leer.

'What look?' he asked with a deceptively innocent air. 'All right. . .' He relented. 'I'm sorry, I couldn't resist it. Those big blue eyes of yours looked so delightfully bemused and bewildered. As if nobody has ever done anything for you before.'

'No one ever has. . .not like this,' she said, deliberately injecting a dry note into her voice for her own self-preservation. 'So. . .why *are* you doing it?' she repeated, determined to pursue it.

He might think she was a dewy-eyed innocent from the suburbs, swept off her feet by his knight-in-shining-armour act, starry-eyed enough to bestow a few feminine favours in return, but he was dead wrong. To get involved with a man like Case Travers would be asking for trouble. Trouble and heartache.

This wasn't a man looking for love or commitment, for anything meaningful or long-term. Under that coat of shining armour, unless she was very much mistaken, beat a cold, unfeeling heart, and he would resist ever entrusting it to another woman. His body maybe—on a casual, fleeting basis—but not his heart. And that wasn't the kind of man she would ever want in her life. David, at least, was *serious* about her. And she would always know precisely where she stood with him.

'I told you. . .it's in my interests to keep my employees happy.' His tone had chilled, as if he wasn't used to having his actions questioned, let alone dissected. 'I saw a chance to play Cupid. Simple as that.' He turned his head away, almost dismissively, and leaned back against the headrest, closing his eyes.

But he hadn't finished, and let his voice, faintly

derisive now, curl past her. 'Whether you decide you
want to marry your friend David or not, he deserves to
know what really happened the other day, don't you
think? And the sooner the better. I've given you that
chance,' he said flatly. 'It's up to you to take it from
here.'

'I'm not ungrateful. . .truly,' she said swiftly, feeling
like kicking herself now. She had misjudged him. He
didn't have any ulterior motive. Maybe—an uncomfortable twinge quivered through her—something deep
down inside *her* had been half hoping. . .wondering. . .
imagining what it would be like. . .

She felt a stab of disloyalty to David. And a rush of
self-reproach mingled—treacherously—with a faint
resentment that she wasn't free to explore her own
feelings. . .even crazily futile ones. She swallowed, and
turned her head to gaze out of the window at the
massed white cloud below.

Yes. . . She stifled a sigh. Case Travers was right. She
had to have it out with David, and the sooner the
better. She must face him. . .talk things over. . .find out
what her true feelings really were. And either say yes
or finish it, once and for all.

The sultry Queensland heat, so different from
Melbourne's late autumn crispness, hit her forcibly as
she stepped off the plane at Coolangatta Airport. She'd
only brought an expandable overnight bag with her,
and the barest of necessities, but it seemed that the few
light, casual things she'd brought would be ample.

It wasn't as if she'd be attending the conference,
needing anything more formal—except, possibly, for
the dinner dance tonight, assuming David wanted her
to go with him. And she'd thrown in a slinky little
number for that, along with a pair of evening sandals.
Anything else she needed, well, as Case said, there
were always the shops.

She peeled off the denim jacket she'd worn on the

plane. She obviously wouldn't be needing jackets or sweaters up here. She felt a nervous flutter at the thought that she was so close to seeing David again. Did she really *want* to see him again, *want* this confrontation? Would it have been better if she'd never come, if she'd decided not to bother to explain?

She found herself hoping, for a fleeting second, that David wouldn't be too overjoyed to see her. It would be so difficult to disappoint him. . .to fob him off again if he decided to sweep her into his arms and demand to have her answer on the spot. She still wasn't ready to *give* him an answer. She simply wanted to explain to him that she hadn't stood him up the other day, and to tell him. . .

She licked suddenly dry lips. It wasn't going to be easy, but she couldn't go on keeping him dangling on a string. It wouldn't be fair. 'Be sure,' her mother kept insisting. Maybe Case Travers was right. Maybe she never would be sure.

'We should arrive at the hotel just before the delegates break for lunch.' Case waved her to a shiny limousine that had been sent for them, and the driver leaped out to take their bags. 'Don't worry, Lucy.' Had he sensed her inner turmoil? 'You'll have ample time to book into your hotel room and freshen up before you meet David.'

His quizzical gaze did a lazy downward sweep, licking over her scoop-necked polo top *and*, if she wasn't mistaken, over the generous curves she'd revealed since removing her jacket, then on down the modest length of her flared denim skirt to dwell a moment on her bare legs, still tanned from their summer exposure, and her pink-toed feet in the strappy leather sandals she'd chosen for the flight.

'Does that look mean I should change for lunch?' she demanded, her skin prickling under his scrutiny.

'A purely appreciative look, I assure you.' His crooked smile flashed briefly, barely long enough to soften the deep lines in his cheeks. 'Stay as you are, by all means. I think you'll find everyone else will be dressed very casually. Even the delegates from the conference.'

'They'll all be lunching together?' she asked, feeling another flutter of nerves. When David's colleagues heard that she'd flown all the way up here to meet him... *Oh, hell*, she thought, feeling the pressure closing in on her again. What am I doing here?

Her panic must have shown in her eyes, because Case touched her arm briefly and said, 'Relax. You're as tight as a spring. This is the sunny Gold Coast, remember. It's all very casual up here. The delegates can lunch where they like, but most choose to have it at the conference hotel, where we're heading now.' He waved her into the back seat of the car, and startled her by climbing in beside her.

As the car swept away he leaned towards her. 'If you're afraid you might miss David at lunchtime, why not wait for him at the door of the conference centre and catch him as he comes out?'

She bit her lip. 'I'd prefer not to be so conspicuous. I think I'll just leave a message for him that I'll be in my room...'

'Rubbish, there's no need to hide yourself away.' The black eyes mocked her. 'If you're concerned about what people will think of you turning up here, we can spread it around that you've just dropped in here on your way to visit your mother. That's true enough, isn't it? You do intend to see her over the weekend?'

'Of course...' She gulped. She would have to ring her mother straight away...warn her that she was here.

But there wasn't time. After checking in at the front desk and being handed their keys—their rooms, she noted, were on different floors, his undoubtedly being the best suite in the hotel—Case bundled her into a lift—an ultra-modern, ultra-fast lift this time—and issued instructions on their way up together. 'Just drop your bag in your room, powder your nose, or whatever, then meet me down in the lobby. I'll take you to the conference centre.'

'You don't have to do—'

'I'll give you five minutes,' he rapped as they reached her floor. 'We might even catch the same lift going down. I have to confess I enjoy sharing lifts with you,' he confided as the doors swung open.

Reminded of the way he'd fooled her into believing he had a phobia about lifts—he'd shown no sign of it a moment ago—she paused as she stepped out and asked sweetly, 'You're sure you'll be all right travelling the rest of the way on your own? You won't need me to hold your hand?'

An appreciative glint flashed in the dark depths of his eyes. 'I'd like that. . .very much,' he said smoothly. 'Only we're running out of time. Five minutes,' he reminded her, and as the lift door closed behind her she heard his voice wafting after her, 'I'll try to be brave.'

She was still smiling as she let herself into her brightly furnished room. Cynical he might be, hardened and scarred by love he might be too, but he'd managed to retain a sense of humour. She missed that in David, she realised. Nice as he was, he'd never been a great one for light-hearted banter or seeing the humorous side of a situation.

She chewed on her lip. It had never really bothered her until now. His good qualities had always out-weighed the odd deficiency she'd perceived in him from time to time. Even in their most intimate moments. . .

But she had no time to think about that now. Her five minutes were rapidly dwindling. She dropped her bag on the bed, pulled out her toilet bag and rushed to the bathroom.

'Well. . .I wasn't expecting you to take me at my word.' Case swept appreciative eyes over her as she joined him in the lobby with seconds to spare.

'Women normally keep you waiting?' she asked sweetly, trying not to react to the dark gleam in his eye.

'Often. . .and with far less effective results,' he said with easy gallantry, bringing a pink tinge to her cheeks—until she remembered who he was and how many times he must have mouthed the same smooth compliment. 'The conference centre's this way. . .' He began steering her away. 'They're obviously not out yet, or this lobby would be chaotic.'

Chaotic. Like her insides at this moment. But were they chaotic at the thought of seeing David again? Or at the thought of Case Travers bowing out of her life, once he'd done his duty by her and handed her over to David? This might be the last time she ever saw him, except at a distance. . .

Inexplicably, her spirits dipped.

'We're just in time.' Case swept her into a broad foyer flanked by doors that at this very moment were being flung wide open. People wearing name-tags— mostly men—began pouring out.

'Please don't let me hold you up,' she pleaded, feeling thoroughly nervous by now. For some reason she didn't want Case Travers witnessing her reunion with David. 'I'll be fine. . . I'll just wait here until I see him.'

'Here he comes now.' Case, in his usual autocratic way, ignored her. 'I'll catch his eye for you.' He had a finger poised, ready to beckon him over.

Lucy strained her neck to see through the crowd. And blinked as she caught sight of David's famliar fair head. His gaze was intent on the person beside him. A woman! He had his hand lightly on her back, steering her through the throng, and they were both laughing and looking very relaxed and cosy together.

'Well. . .your friend has found some consolation, it seems, in his hour of need,' Case said drily from beside her. 'Oh, don't worry, Lucy.' His eyes flicked to hers, a mocking light in them. 'I'm sure it's entirely innocent.

It's Sally Richmond, from our research laboratory in Sydney. A delightful girl. Quiet and hard-working. They're probably discussing eucalypt fibres.'

He caught her arm as he spoke, and dragged her over to join the two of them. The look on David's face when he saw her, and saw Case Travers *with* her, made her for some crazy reason want to burst into hysterical giggles. At the same time she wished the floor would open up and swallow her, wished she'd never agreed to come, wished she'd left things as they were. David would have survived. Obviously!

'I've brought a surprise for you, David,' Case said easily, his strongly carved face coolly impassive. But Lucy could sense that he was enjoying this. . .and it made her want to hit him.

Why *was* he going to such lengths to reunite them? Out of the goodness of his heart? From her observation of him so far, Case Travers *had* no heart. As Cupid, he just didn't ring true.

'Lucy!' David croaked. 'What are you doing here?'

'Lucy has come up to visit her mother for the weekend,' Case put in swiftly, adding after the slightest pause, 'And you too, of course. As it happened, I had a spare air ticket, and after the experience we both shared the other day—' now he allowed a hint of humour to shimmer in his dark eyes '—she was prepared to trust me enough to fly up with me.'

David stared at him blankly and then turned to face Lucy, his soft hazel eyes appealing to her for enlightenment. He was obviously dying to ask about the experience they'd both shared, but seemed daunted by the fact that she had shared it with his *el supremo*.

'I'll let Lucy explain to you over lunch,' Case said coolly. 'Forgive me, Sally. . .' His eyes swept to David's stunned companion, a gentle-looking young woman with a thin, pale face, big brown eyes and smooth brown hair. 'Lucy Farrell. . .Sally Richmond.' Case made the brief introduction with a wave of his hand.

'Well, Lucy. . .' He swung back to her, an inscrutable glint in his eye. 'You and David go off and have lunch together. Grab a quiet table for two somewhere. Sally, you come with me. I'm meeting some of our colleagues in the grill room. . .you can join us.'

The big boss taking charge, making decisions, dispensing commands, Lucy thought, bristling.

'No doubt we'll all meet up again at the dinner dance tonight,' Case said pleasantly as he ushered a bemused Sally away. '*Ciao!*'

'*Ciao!*' Lucy echoed, her tone faintly caustic, her eyes sending tiny daggers into the back of his white shirt as he strode away. He might think this was all vastly amusing, but she didn't. She wasn't looking forward to the next hour or so. And Case Travers, damn him, was fully aware of it!

'You mean you *were* on your way up to meet me the other day?' David stared across the small restaurant table at her. He'd chosen a quiet corner of the hotel's roof garden restaurant for lunch. 'It was only the lift getting stuck that prevented you?'

She nodded, her teeth tugging at her lip. 'David, I—'

'You must have been cutting it pretty fine anyway.' David's face tightened, his tone faintly puzzled. 'I waited for you down in the lobby until five to twelve. When you hadn't shown up by then, I jumped in the lift and rushed up to Kowalsky's, thinking that maybe you'd arrived *earlier* than I had and were already up there ahead of me. . .waiting.'

His mouth twisted. 'You weren't, of course.' His hazel eyes showed his hurt. 'You were obviously in no hurry to meet me on time. Even knowing I'd given you a. . .deadline.'

She took a deep breath. 'Maybe a girl doesn't like having a gun pointed at her head. Even so. . .I did come. I reached the lobby a minute or two before twelve. I must have just missed you before you caught the lift up.'

He stuck out his lower lip. 'I had to do something decisive to get a decision out of you, one way or the other. I want to get *married*, Lu. I'm thirty-two years old and I'm ready to settle down. And you're twenty-six, with a successful practice of your own. You're not exactly just out of college. We've been together for over a year...you know me as well as you ever will. You ought to know your own mind by now.'

'You're right,' she mumbled. 'I should.' Obviously he didn't think that sex counted in getting to know a person. David didn't believe in sex before marriage, or at least not in going all the way, and she'd gone along with him—probably because he'd never aroused her to the point of feeling frustrated.

'Why were you coming to meet me at all,' David demanded, 'if you still weren't sure?'

She swallowed. 'I guess...because you're a lovely guy and I didn't want to risk losing you.'

He pursed his lips, his eyes flickering. 'Tell me, Lucy,' he said quietly. 'What if that lift you were in hadn't broken down? What if you *had* arrived before I left? I waited nearly half an hour—until twelve-twenty-five—before I left...without realising you were stuck in the other lift on your way up. Well?'

She found it hard to meet his eye, but she forced herself to do so. 'I... I wouldn't have let you buy me a ring,' she admitted, determined to be honest with him. 'I realised as I drove in to meet you that I still wasn't ready to...commit myself. Irrevocably.' She saw him stiffen, sensed his withdrawal, and reached across the table to cover the hand he'd curled around his glass before he could pull it away.

'I—I didn't want you waiting at Kowalsky's and having me not turn up...thinking I'd stood you up,' she was quick to add. 'David, believe me, if I'd made up my mind beforehand not to—not to accept your ring, I would have rung and told you so. . .before you went into town. But I. . .still wasn't sure. I didn't want to lose you,' she said in a rush, feeling thoroughly wretched by now. She *didn't* want to lose him. . .as a friend. That was the truth of it. But any more than that. . . She looked at David helplessly.

'But you don't know that you *want* me either,' David said tightly. 'Not for ever.'

She sighed, and drew back her hand. 'I'm not being fair to you, I know,' she said miserably, bowing her head and gazing at a wine stain on the tablecloth. 'I don't know why you're being so patient with me. I don't deserve it.'

'I love you, that's why,' he muttered. 'But I need to know that you love me as much. I don't believe in one-sided relationships.' Was he thinking of her parents? 'Look. . .maybe, when we get back home, we should take a break from each other for a while.'

Her head jerked up. She'd been working up to suggesting the very same thing! She'd been trying to find the right words so as not to hurt him too much. And now *he*—

'But it doesn't mean we can't enjoy the dinner dance tonight,' David added swiftly. 'Or stop being friends. . .'

She smiled weakly in relief, feeling the pressure on her easing. He hadn't closed the door. . .hadn't created a scene. But then, David wouldn't. He was far too gentle. . .too nice. She let her eyes tell him so.

'And you'll come with me tomorrow when I visit my mother?' she asked tentatively. 'I intend to hire a car and drive to Brisbane. . .assuming she's going to be home, of course. I haven't rung her yet.'

'You haven't?' He looked surprised. 'Why not?'

She drew in her breath. 'Case suggested I surprise her. Only I'm not sure Mum would appreciate a surprise visit, so I'm planning to ring her from here this afternoon. I hope *you* didn't mind me springing this visit on you, David?' she asked anxiously, curiosity prompting her to add, 'You were about to have lunch with. . .Sally, weren't you?'

Two blotches of colour stained his cheeks. 'Oh, it was just that she. . .we're colleagues, that's all.' He shrugged, adding after a pause, 'She's nice. She won't mind.' He flashed a smile. 'Of course I'm delighted you're here. I appreciate it very much, Lu. . .that you came all this way to explain.'

She couldn't claim the credit. 'Thank Case Travers,' she said, flushing. 'It was his idea to fly me up here. His idea to surprise you. It seemed to amuse him to. . .' she hesitated '. . .to play Cupid, as he put it.' To play puppet-master, more like, she thought, with a flash of resentment.

'You told him about my ultimatum?' The pink blotches deepened to red.

'No. Well, not until he. . . David, he overhead me mention your name to Mr Kowalsky, and he started asking questions. It. . .sort of came out. I—I'm sorry,' she said.

'So now he knows my girlfriend can't make up her mind about me,' David said, his tone brooding now.

'David, no! I never told him that!' But Case had guessed. . .

'But he wanted to play Cupid, you said. . .'

'Because he knew I'd missed my appointment with you! He wanted us to have a chance to sort things out. He said he likes to look after his employees. . .'

'In matters that are work-related. . .yes. But he normally doesn't involve himself in our *personal* affairs. Why would he put himself out to help *us*?' David shook his head. 'It's just not like him. He has a reputation for being cold-hearted. . .a cynic. . .being hard to get to know. And—' he lowered his voice '—for treating women with contempt. He'll play around with them, shower them with attention and expensive trinkets, but he'll make sure he never gets emotionally involved. He doesn't trust women. Hasn't since his divorce.'

There was condemnation in his voice. David didn't approve of divorce. Another reason she'd wanted to be quite sure before committing herself to him. With her family's record, she didn't want to go into a marriage with him unless she was confident it would last. . .for ever.

'So. . .you'll drive up to Brisbane with me tomorrow, when I visit my mother?' she asked again, wanting to shift the conversation away from divorce. And away from Case Travers?

'Sorry, Lu, I can't. I have to fly back home first thing in the morning. Our plant manager's off to the States tomorrow, to look at a new packaging plant we're putting in over there. I'm to be acting plant manager while he's away. It means we'll only have tonight, Lu. I can't even skip this afternoon's sessions—I have to give a paper.'

She met his eyes for a long moment. They both knew what he meant. After the dinner dance tonight they wouldn't be seeing each other again. At least, not until she was ready to admit that she wanted him back. For good. Ready to make a lifetime commitment. Assuming, of course, that he would take her back, would *want* her back.

In the meantime—she felt a vague flutter of relief—she had some breathing space. It was all she wanted.

Almost traitorously, she found herself wondering if Case Travers would remember the promise she'd light-heartedly extracted from him to partner her in a dance this evening or if he would ignore her from now on. . . now that he'd done his duty by her.

CHAPTER FOUR

THE ballroom foyer, where pre-dinner drinks were being served, was rapidly filling with people. There was a predominance of males, though many of the delegates had obviously brought wives or girlfriends to the conference.

Lucy couldn't see Case Travers. If he'd been there, she would have picked him out easily. With his height and imposing presence, he was a man who would stand out in any crowd.

'Looking for someone?' David asked from beside her. He seemed vaguely put out that she wasn't giving her full attention to him on their last night together as a couple.

She turned back to him with a quick smile. 'Just wondering where your boss was. . .Case Travers,' she said lightly. 'And your friend Sally,' she added as an afterthought, realising that she couldn't see her either.

'Some of the delegates were going to a machinery manufacturer's cocktail party beforehand.' David's gaze swept the crowd. 'Case must have— Ah, there's Sally!' He brightened noticeably. 'Let's join her, shall we?'

'Sure.' As David grabbed her hand and pulled her across the foyer she wondered why she didn't feel a tug of jealousy. David isn't the two-timing type, that's why, she told herself tartly. And Sally's just a colleague.

'Hello, David. . .Lucy,' Sally greeted them, her big brown eyes a trifle guarded, Lucy thought, as they met hers. 'You look lovely,' she added, with what sounded like genuine warmth as she took in the svelte simplicity of Lucy's platinum satin-charmeuse shift dress and the honeyed tan of her bare arms and shoulders.

'So do you,' Lucy said, and meant it. Sally had struck her earlier in the day as pleasant-looking but rather shy and mousy, but tonight, with a touch of added make-up and a glittering top to give a lift to her pearl-coloured skirt, she *was* lovely, Lucy realised. Yet she still felt no pang at having a possible rival.

'You both look fantastic,' David said gallantly. 'I hope we're all at the same table. There's a list on that board by the door. . .let's take a look.'

There was still no sign of Case Travers even after they'd found their table in the sumptuous chandelier-lit ballroom—all three of them having been placed, as they'd hoped, at the same table. Lucy had felt a treacherous stab of disappointment that Case Travers' name hadn't been on the list for their table for ten.

She had David on one side of her and a balding, middle-aged man called Arthur, an industrial chemist from a New Zealand paper company, on her left. She wondered, when she saw Sally on David's right, if the two of them had requested to be seated together before her arrival.

'Here come the bigwigs. The official party.' Arthur nudged her as a procession of half a dozen men, all looking distinguished in dinner suits with special badges on their lapels, passed by their table, accompanied by four women of varying ages in full evening dress.

Lucy's heart gave a tiny flip as she saw that Case Travers was one of the men. As her gaze followed his easy, fluid progress to the official table she heard a faint buzz around her own table, and she sensed that all eyes were on the official party. . .and on Case Travers in particular, she didn't doubt. He was without a doubt the most arrestingly attractive, most sexy-looking, most imposing man of the bunch. And, as head of one of Australia's biggest privately owned companies, one of the wealthiest, most successful, most eligible men in the ballroom.

And she had dared demand that he keep a dance for

her! What a laugh, she thought derisively. He'll be sticking with the conference officials, the other big company bosses and those glamour pusses at his table, not seeking *you* out, Lucy Farrell.

As she felt a vague slide in her spirits—he'd be wonderful to dance with, she just knew it—she saw him turn his head, almost as if he'd sensed her eyes on him, and acknowledge her with a slight inclination of his dark head. Which had the instant effect of making *her* the focus of all eyes at her table—being noticed, singled out. She gave a quick, careless smile and turned back to David.

But all through dinner she was pricklingly aware of Case Travers' presence at the top table. Acutely aware of him, as if every other person in the room had faded by comparison. Not that she so much as glanced in his direction. She made sure she didn't! David deserved to have all her attention tonight. Even if he was giving a fair share of *his* attention to Sally, on his right, forcing Lucy to suffer the rather tedious patter of the New Zealander on her left.

She found herself wishing the dinner would end.

There was dancing throughout the evening, between courses, but no one from Lucy's table seemed interested for the first half of the evening—perhaps because the men outnumbered the women by eight to two and preferred to talk business. She saw Case Travers on the dance floor each time the band struck up, and each time he was partnering a different woman from the official table. She found herself wishing. . . imagining. . .

'You look as if you'd love to have a dance.' The New Zealander's voice from beside her sent her thoughts skittering.

Her head snapped round. 'Oh, no. . .not really,' she said, adding with a light laugh, 'I'm happy just watching. Besides—' she dropped her voice '—David hates dancing.'

'Ah, then, please. . .allow me.' With a beaming smile Arthur pushed back his chair and held out a hand.

She summoned a smile and let him lead her onto the dance floor. At least it would be a change from his dreary chatter.

Glancing back at her table, she was amazed to see that David was also rising, drawing Sally to her feet.

'I guess we've shamed him into it,' Arthur remarked, following her gaze.

She nodded. 'I guess we have.' Her gaze now, of its own volition, was skimming over the other couples on the dance floor. . .eventually colliding, as if drawn by some magnetic force, with a pair of glittering black eyes. She saw a dark eyebrow quirk, as if in surprise that she had finally stepped onto the dance floor but not with David. She saw his gaze slide past her, and knew that he'd seen David with Sally. Now he must be really wondering, she thought, with a wry quirk of her lips.

They hadn't been on the dance floor for long when the band signalled the end of the set, and Arthur, with an audible sigh, steered her back to her table, where a delicious meringue and tropical fruit salad dessert lay waiting. The official speeches and an award presentation followed. Once they were over, the band struck up again for the final medley of the evening, and David leaned towards her.

'When there are a few more people on the dance floor, Lu. . .' His voice trailed off, his handsome face breaking into a surprised smile as he glanced over her right shoulder.

Lucy turned to see Case Travers bearing down on them.

She felt her stomach swoop, her nerves tense. Was he coming to claim her for the dance she'd recklessly demanded? What would David and everyone else at her table think if he did? Not that she could imagine a man like Case Travers caring what people thought. She had a feeling that nothing would stop this man doing whatever he wanted to do. But it was more likely he was coming over simply to be sociable.

The thought was confirmed when, instead of singling her out, his gaze swept over the three of them—David, Sally and herself.

'I'm inviting all of our Maxi Board people to join me for a nightcap at the poolside bar after we finish up here.' He smiled easily, appearing in no doubt that they would jump at the invitation. Which both Sally and David promptly did. Royal command, Lucy thought, with a whimsical glance up at him.

'And you too, Lucy. . .of course.' Now the black gaze did single her out, darkly powerful, serenely compelling, the smouldering depths making her feel in that second the way she was sure he could make all women feel—as if she were the only woman in the room.

'Thank you,' she managed, expecting him to turn on his heel and move on. But instead he held out his hand. 'I promised you a dance, Lucy, I believe. . .' His eyes gleamed in gentle mockery, reminding her that she had asked *him*!

She felt warmth flooding her cheeks, aware of the heightened interest around the table. 'I was only kidding,' she said quickly. 'You don't have to—'

'My pleasure, I assure you.'

Unsure if he was patronising her, or simply complying out of a sense of chivalrous duty, she rose from her chair, pretending not to see his outstretched hand. She was sure he wouldn't have meant her to take it anyway. He'd hardly want David or anyone else thinking he'd singled her out for any *personal* reason!

But reasons and motives seemed unimportant the moment he took her into his arms and twirled her expertly round the not yet crowded dance floor. She felt as light as air, as if her feet were barely touching the floor, as if her body was floating in space. They moved in perfect unison, as if made for each other, as if nothing around them existed. She felt her cheek brush against his shoulder as they swirled in time to the music, felt his hand warmly intimate on her back, his fingers sliding over the smooth satin of her dress.

Never before had a dance felt so sublime, so romantic, so right. Or so potently sensuous. She glanced up at him, and as her gaze briefly caught his she sensed that he felt the same. . .

She blinked and looked away. She had to be imagining it! He probably made all women feel this way—and was perfectly aware of it.

'The way you dance, I'm surprised you've been content to sit out for most of the evening,' he drawled, swinging her round in a mind-spinning arc.

He'd been *watching* her? She gave a careless laugh, her soft hair swirling in the air, her eyes a sparkling turquoise. With him as her partner, she would have happily danced all night!

As the music changed its beat to a slower, more pedestrian tempo, he drew back a little. Deliberately? she wondered, still feeling breathless—and knowing it had nothing to do with a lack of air.

'Well, Lucy. . .' He eyed her sideways, his expression quizzical as he held her away from him, swaying with her in one spot. 'Are you glad I insisted on flying you up here?'

Her clear blue eyes met his without wavering. . . though it wasn't easy. 'It was very good of you,' she said evasively. 'Thank you.'

'That's not what I asked.' An ironic smile touched his lips. 'I haven't seen you dancing with David all evening,' he added pointedly. 'When you did finally step onto the dance floor, I imagined it would have been with him, not some balding, middle-aged New Zealander.'

She shrugged a honey-bronzed shoulder. 'David hates dancing. He has to be practically dragged onto the dance floor. Arthur must have shamed him into it.'

Case gave an imperceptible shake of his head as he glanced across at David and Sally, the two of them deep in conversation as they shuffled around. He growled, 'What's wrong with David. . .turning his back on you for half the night and then insipidly handing you over to other men to dance with? If you were my woman, I wouldn't let you out of my sight. I'd have you on the floor all night!'

It was so unexpected—the *way* he said it, the low rumble of passion in his voice—that she felt her legs turning to liquid beneath her, and was grateful that he had his arm curved round her spine.

And why—she felt heat flare into her cheeks—did she get the feeling that as he'd said 'on the floor all night' he wasn't thinking of a *dance* floor?

She tried to pull herself together. He's not thinking of *you*, you fool, she told herself. He's just exasperated with David, letting you know the way *he* would operate if he was in David's place.

'If David could dance as well as you,' she retorted drily, 'he probably would.' Let him think it was only his expertise on the dance floor that she found exhilarating, not *him*.

By now the dance floor was packed, everyone wanting to join in for the final dance of the night. Lucy found herself pushed up against Case's chest, being bumped and jostled from all sides, barely able to move.

'How did you two meet in the first place?' Case asked, curiosity now the only note she could detect in his voice. 'I gather he's not one for competing in triathlons, like you, or spending his time at the gym?'

'No.' The very thought made her smile. 'David came to my clinic one day with. . .with a foot problem.'

'Ah. But not a sports injury, by the sound of it?'

She shook her head. 'No, it was. . .another problem.' She hesitated, then added primly, 'There is such a thing as patient confidentiality.' David might not appreciate having his boss find out that he'd once suffered from a painful ingrown toenial.

'By all means. . .keep his terrible secret. One's feet are. . .sacred.' The black eyes glimmered under the dark brows. 'So. . .' He eased her out of the crush, to the outer edge of the dance floor. 'Am I to take it the two of you are happily back together again?'

She flicked a look up at him and saw that his eyes had narrowed, masking whatever thoughts lay behind them. Had he sensed that all was still not right between them?

She moistened her lips with a flick of her tongue. 'We're still friends, if that's what you mean.'

'You're saying David's retracted his ultimatum for the time being? Given you some extra breathing space?' His tone was lazily indifferent now, as if the subject was beginning to bore him.

'Something like that.' She hesitated to tell him that she and David had agreed to part company altogether after tonight. He might get the idea—heaven forbid— that she was *ditching* David, leaving her way free to set her cap at. . .at a far bigger fish!

'Is he going with you tomorrow when you visit your mother?' Case asked in the same careless tone.

'He can't. He has to fly back to Melbourne first thing in the morning to deputise for his plant manager, who's flying to America tomorrow. It means David has to be on call over the weekend.'

'Ah. . .yes. His manager's off to inspect our new packaging plant in the States.' He spoke as if he'd forgotten, but Lucy sensed that Case Travers wasn't the type of boss who would forget what his senior managers were doing. Or who was deputising for them. He must have known all along that David had to fly home first thing in the morning. He'd probably contrived it himself!

Her head snapped up at the thought, but she saw nothing in his eyes to suggest such a thing. But then. . .Case Travers was clever enough to hide any emotion. If he *had* emotions.

As the dance ended with a dramatic drumroll Case said blithely, 'Not to worry, I'll drive you to your mother's. As it happens, I'll be spending the weekend up in Brisbane myself. I have friends I want to catch up with.'

She felt as if her breath had been sucked from her body. He was offering to drive her there himself? It took a moment before she could gulp in a lungful of air. 'Well. . .thanks,' she forced out, 'I'd appreciate it. If you'll just—just drop me off in town I can catch a bus to Avril's place, where my mother lives. They're out a bit, on the way to the airport.'

'Rubbish, I'll drop you off at your mother's; it won't be out of my way.' He was steering her from the dance floor as he spoke. 'Does your mother know you're coming?' he asked. 'Or did you do as I suggested and decide to surprise her?'

'My mother's not a great one for surprises.' She tossed her head, to show him that not everyone jumped to his every command. 'I did try to ring her after lunch today, and again early this evening, but there was no answer.'

'You think she's away?' There was a sharpness in his voice that made Lucy glance curiously up at him. Why should he care if her mother had gone away for the weekend? Unless. . . Her heart picked up a beat. Unless he *wanted* her to drive up to Brisbane with him. . .and would be disappointed if she didn't!

'I. . .I doubt if she'd be away.' She hoped her voice didn't sound as shaky as she felt. 'From memory, Friday's the day Mum and Avril often go into town for the day. They like to browse around, have lunch, and then take in a film or a show. They must have done that. . . They weren't at home by six o'clock, when I tried last. I'll call again first thing in the morning.'

'Well. . .if you think it's necessary.' He obviously

didn't. 'We could just call in on the off-chance, and if your mother's still not at home—if she's stayed over-night somewhere—you could spend the day with me. I can catch up with my friends on Sunday. Or some other time.'

As she caught her breath at the offer he went on smoothly, 'If your mother's still not home by evening I'll see that you're safely booked in somewhere over-night and we'll check her out again the next day. We'll have virtually all day Sunday in Brisbane; we're not booked to fly home until late afternoon. She's bound to be home by then.'

Without waiting for an answer—even if she'd been capable of giving one—he swept her to her table, where the others were already on their feet, making their final farewells. The surrounding tables were beginning to break up too, with people already wandering off.

'See you at the poolside bar. . .the three of you,' Case reminded them as he reunited her with David and Sally, before turning on his heel and heading back to his own table.

Lucy, plucking her eyes away from his dark head and powerful physique, caught David stifling a yawn.

'If it wasn't the big boss inviting us,' he muttered as he caught her eye, 'I'd be heading for the sack. I have to catch an early flight in the morning and it's after midnight already.'

David had never been one for late nights. He started work early and liked to retire reasonably early. Though tonight. . . Lucy eyed him speculatively, her heart heavy with self-reproach. Maybe he wasn't tired at all, just anxious to get away from *her*. Knowing it was over, knowing that this was their last time spent together—at least until she made up her mind whether or not she wanted him back. *Would* she want him back? she wondered, very much doubting it.

'I'm sure your big boss won't expect us to stay for long,' she consoled him, not looking forward to the moment when she would have to say goodnight and goodbye to David. Not that David was the emotional type, likely to go to pieces or to pine away with a broken heart. Knowing him, he'd be as stolid and stalwart as ever. Accepting it as he accepted most things.

But as they made their way to the poolside bar it wasn't her qualms over parting from David that was causing her heart to race, her chest to heave, her hands to tremble. It was the memory of Case's arms around her on the dance floor, the memory of his black eyes glinting above hers, the dreamy feeling that they were still floating around the floor as if they were one.

Why had she never felt like this with David?

Because David can't dance like Case Travers, that's all it is, you fool, she told herself firmly. She gave herself a brisk shake.

In the same moment she caught sight of Case Travers' tall, imposing figure silhouetted against the floodlit pool, his head bent over a woman in a white strapless gown. And reality began to seep back. That magical dance wouldn't have meant anything special to Case Travers, that was for sure. He would dance the same way with every woman he swept onto the dance floor. . .would make each one feel the way he'd made *her* feel. That was the kind of man he was.

'Ah. . .' Case turned his head as the three of them approached. He signalled to a passing waiter. 'Let's drink to a successful conference,' he said, plucking brimming champagne glasses from the waiter's loaded tray.

Lucy knew that David normally avoided champagne, claiming it made him fuzzy in the head. He preferred to stick to beer. But tonight, surprisingly, he made no demur as Case handed him a glass, echoing Case's sentiments as he raised his glass to his lips—'To the conference!'—and even proposing a toast of his own. 'And to our new packaging plant in the States!'

Case nodded approvingly, drifting off minutes later to do his hostly duty elsewhere. David waved his glass, insisting on another toast. 'To Sally's new work with eucalypt fibres!'

Sally blushed.

As the two launched into a discussion on the research Sally was doing Lucy's gaze drifted of its own accord to where Case was weaving from one group to another, attracting smiles and adoration—and apparent respect—wherever he went.

Was this the man whose ex-wife had accused him of being dull and boring, with anti-social tendencies? she mused. He couldn't have looked more at ease, couldn't have been a more relaxed, attentive host—joking and chatting easily with the people who worked for him, ensuring that everyone was well looked after and having a good time.

Since those present were all Maxi Board people, or were partnering Maxi Board people, there was much mingling and plenty of high spirits and laughter. With a successful conference behind them, and tonight being the last evening most of them would be spending in their balmy sub-tropical paradise, they were letting their hair down.

David most of all, Lucy noticed. He was acting quite out of character, downing one glass of champagne after another as he dragged Sally and herself from group to group.

Case would breeze over every now and then, to enquire how they were, his brow rising fractionally as he noted what was happening to David. He was fading fast, swaying ominously where he stood, his eyelids drooping over decidedly bleary eyes. Soon he was almost alseep on his feet!

'Hey. . .David, old man, don't fall asleep on us.' Case touched him on the shoulder.

David jumped to at least partial alert. ''Course not,'

he muttered, slurring the words. 'Having a great ol' time.'

'Don't you have to catch the early flight in the morning?' Case asked solicitously, though Lucy, eyes narrowing, would have sworn there was a glimmer of mocking amusement in his eyes.

'That's right,' David mumbled, swaying on his feet. 'Early. . .far too early. Guessh I'd better call it a night.'

'Good idea.' Case's eyes glinted agreement. 'Without sleep you'll be useless at the plant tomorrow. By all means turn in, David. Lucy and Sally will be fine. . . I'll make sure they're looked after.'

Lucy felt a frisson of alarm. Looked after? Even. . . maybe. . .personally escorted back to their rooms? She shot him a quick, suspicious look. Was this what he'd been leading up to when he'd asked her to dance, when he'd offered her a lift to Brisbane tomorrow, when he'd suggested spending the whole day with her if necessary. . . And the *night*? Did he think, with David out of the way. . .?

She almost laughed aloud at the wildly unlikely notion. She was sinking into the realms of fantasy! And yet—her heart skipped a beat—Case Travers did have a reputation for having brief, meaningless affairs, for amusing himself with women he didn't care about—at least not deeply or for long. Maybe that 'If you were my woman' remark of his on the dance floor had meant more than she'd thought!

As she gulped in a shaky breath she heard David mumble thickly, 'Well. . .if you don't mind.' He seemed relieved that Case wasn't urging him to stay, anxious to be on his way. Which made Lucy wonder if he'd deliberately drunk himself into a near stupor so that he'd have an excuse to make an early escape. To avoid having to leave with *her* and face a painful parting in private? 'Lu. . .' He turned bleary eyes in her direction. 'You don't mind, do you?'

'Of course not,' she said at once. She gave him a

specially warm smile and stepped closer, dropping her voice. 'We must keep in touch,' she said, wanting him to know that she still cared about him, that their decision to part didn't mean they couldn't be friends and have occasional contact.

David swayed over her. 'Yesh, we must.' He brushed her cheek with a sloppy kiss, tottering slightly as he drew back. 'G'night, Sally. . .Case. Great night.' He raised an unsteady hand and stumbled away, bumping into a poolside table as he headed for the glass doors leading into the hotel.

'Looks like he could do with a helping hand.' Case tossed them a whimsical smile. 'We don't want him crashing through those glass doors.' He swung after him, catching him up in a couple of long, fluid strides, carefully supporting David through the doorway.

Lucy bit down on her lip as she gazed after them, hardly knowing whether to giggle or groan. In any other circumstances the sight of staid, steady David reeling from too much alcohol might have tickled her sense of humour. But at this moment she felt more contrite than amused.

'Maybe I should have gone with him,' she confided to Sally with a sigh. 'Only I. . .don't think he wanted me to.' After a second's hesitation she explained, 'We've decided not to see each other for a while. . .to give each other some space. It's all a bit awkward.'

Sally's big brown eyes widened. With more than surprise, Lucy sensed. With hope, maybe? 'You have?' The girl paused a moment, then admitted in a rush, 'David did tell me when he first arrived up here that he—that he thought it was all off between you. He was pretty down,' she revealed. 'I think that's why he. . . confided in me. But then, when you turned up here. . . Well, I gathered you'd patched things up.'

Lucy sighed. 'I'm afraid not. We realised we weren't going anywhere, and a cooling-off period was the best thing. In fact, it was David's idea.' Surely, she mused, if he'd been head over heels in love with her, he would never have suggested it. He'd have put up some kind of fight. . .shown at least some pain or anger or passion. . .some emotion.

Sally's gaze drifted back to the glass doors through which Case and David had vanished.

'I've never seen David drunk before,' Sally said, adding hastily, 'We've bumped into each other at the odd company function or conference. I've never seen him drink much. I guess he was. . .drowning his sorrows,' she went on, a pensive light in her eyes.

'Oh, I don't think it was that,' Lucy said, hoping it wasn't. 'I think he just felt the need to let his hair down a bit after giving his paper today, and he made the mistake of drinking champagne instead of his usual beer.' She tensed as Case reappeared, gulping in relief as a couple from another group grabbed his attention.

'Yes. . .I guess that was it.' Sally visibly brightened. 'It was good of Case to take David to his room. He's a terrific boss. He looks after his employees.'

Does he? Lucy pondered dubiously. Or had he just wanted to make sure that David was out of the way for the night? Well, if he thought he could move in himself now. . .

Her throat constricted as she saw Case heading their way.

'Well. . .' Case winked at Lucy as he joined them. 'I imagine young David will have a sore head when he flies off to Melbourne in the morning.'

And much you care, Lucy thought sourly. She lifted her chin. 'It's time I was heading off too,' she said, looking round for somewhere to put her glass, which was still half filled with champagne. 'Sally, are you—?'

'Oh, don't go yet. . .finish your drinks,' Case drawled. '*You* don't have to leave early in the morning. Unless ten's too early for you, Lucy?' he asked, his tone teasingly casual, as if he didn't care who knew he was giving her a lift to Brisbane the next day. 'I don't imagine you'll want to descend on your mother too early?' he added silkily. Was he letting Sally know *why* he was offering her a lift?

He was also assuming that her mother would be home.

'No. . .ten will be fine. Thank you,' Lucy said politely. 'And thank you for the drinks. Goodnight, Case,' she added firmly, seizing her chance as a middle-aged couple who were also ready to leave plucked at Case's arm from behind.

'I'll say goodnight too,' Sally piped up as Case swung away, making no attempt, Lucy noted with relief, to delay either of them further, merely raising a hand in an easy salute.

Fool, Lucy chided herself as she and Sally dumped their glasses on a poolside table and made their escape. To imagine even for a second that Case Travers might have some rakish intent in mind. . .let alone *here*, in a hotel full of Maxi Board people and with hundreds of other people from the paper industry staying at the same hotel! Talk about living in fantasyland! If the great Case Travers wanted to chase after a woman, she wouldn't be an unworldly suburban podiatrist!

She dragged in a jagged breath as she thought of her trip to Brisbane with Case the next day, his offer to spend the whole day with her if necessary—and to book her in somewhere *overnight* if her mother was still not at home by evening. Would he book himself in too? There wouldn't be a hotel full of Maxi Board people in Brisbane! The thought was enough to start her heart thumping chaotically all over again.

'I hope David's all right.' Sally's gentle eyes showed her concern as they rode up in the lift together—both having rooms, they'd found, on the same floor.

'I would imagine he's sleeping like a baby,' Lucy said drily, hoping it was true. She would hate to think of him having a sleepless night over her. . .because she'd been unwilling to make a commitment to him.

But as she reached the sanctuary of her room and slipped between the cool sheets at last it wasn't David she was thinking about before sleep finally claimed her. She was thinking of driving to Brisbane with Case Travers in the morning. . .just the two of them. And possibly, just possibly, spending the rest of the day with him. And the evening. . .

She snuggled her face deeper into her pillow. No. She'd be crazy to want to see more of him. They had absolutely nothing in common. Their lives were poles apart. He was out of her league in every way. And she wasn't his type.

But, if she wasn't, why would he *want* to spend his whole day with her, when he had friends he could be visiting? Why was he putting himself out for her? *Why?*

CHAPTER FIVE

SHE slept in until after eight, skipping breakfast to catch up on her lost sleep. The first thing she did on waking was call her mother. This time, thankfully, she got through.

'Hello?'

'Hi, Mum, it's me. . .how are you?'

'Lucy! Well, this is a surprise. I usually hear pips when you ring. Where are you calling from?'

'I'm at Surfers. I flew up yesterday for the last day of David's pulp and paper conference.'

'You're up *here*? In *Queensland*? Well, that's wonderful, dear. Any hope of me seeing you? Will you have time to come to Brisbane while you're here?'

'I'll be driving up this morning, as a matter of fact. I've been offered a lift.'

'A lift? Um. . .David's coming with you?' Charlotte's voice cooled almost imperceptibly. She'd never thought that David was the right man for her daughter, had never believed that Lucy cared deeply enough for him. How right she had been.

'David had to fly home this morning.' She would explain later what had happened between them. 'No. . . Case Travers has offered to drive me up.'

'Case *Travers*?' Her mother's voice sharpened. 'You mean. . . The Maxi Board Case Travers?'

'That's right. David's boss.' Her brow puckered at the harsh displeasure in her mother's voice. 'Case has to drive up to—'

'You call him *Case*?' Charlotte cut in. 'I wasn't aware you even knew him.'

'We met the other day. Mum, I'll tell you about it when I see you.' Now wasn't the time to go into details.

'It's no big deal. Case happened to be driving up to
Brisbane this morning and offered to drop me off at
your place. . .simple as that. It doesn't mean you have
to start cleaning the house from top to bottom. It's
highly unlikely he'll come in.'

There was silence for a second. Then her mother
said, 'You're coming up this *morning*, you said?
Today?'

'Leaving here at ten. Yes. Why?' Her mother
sounded decidedly odd today.

'Oh, dear, I'm such a goose! I won't be here.'
Charlotte heaved a sigh. 'I—I wasn't thinking for a
minute. You sprang it on me, dear. Avril and I are
going away for the weekend. A—a scenic bus tour.
Leaving this morning. We won't be back until—until
early next week.' She sounded flustered and unlike her
usual self, Lucy thought in some bemusement. 'Dear,
I'm sorry. . .'

'Mum, calm down, it doesn't matter.' Lucy was quick
to reassure her. 'If you're not going to be there—' her
mind raced ahead '—I might as well fly home. I'll come
up again another time.' Not much point in driving up
to Brisbane with Case now that she knew her mother
wasn't going to be there. She stifled a sigh.

'Yes, *do* come again soon, dear. For my birthday, if
you can. I'd love that.' Charlotte sounded relieved, but
then caught her breath as if something had struck her.
'You don't think Mr Travers will try to talk you into
driving up here with him anyway, do you?' She sounded
anxious.

Lucy frowned. 'Mum, if you think there's something
going on between Case and me—'

'You're saying there isn't? How come David didn't
stay for the weekend?'

'He's on call at the plant. Mum, I thought you didn't
want David in my life,' Lucy bit out in exasperation.

'I've never said that!' Charlotte denied. 'All I've said
is to be sure. . .not to commit yourself until you are.'

Lucy sighed. 'Well, I'm not sure, and I've told David so and we're not going to see each other again for a while. . .if ever,' she let loose in a rush. '*Now* are you satisfied?'

'It's Case Travers. . .isn't it?' Her mother sounded anything *but* satisfied. There was even a note of alarm in her voice. 'Somehow or other that man's turned your head. You think I can't sense it? You're my daughter! Darling, men like Case Travers *devour* women. They use them and then toss them aside. He's had one wrecked marriage already. And they say he's avoiding another like the plague. He's just out for—for what he can get. He leaves broken hearts in his wake wherever he goes.'

'Oh, Mum, where did you hear all that? He *hasn't* turned my head.' Lucy gulped. 'All he's done is offer me a lift to Brisbane this morning. And if you're not going to be there, well. . . I'll fly back home and he'll drive up without me. So you can calm down, OK? Mum, I have to go now. I'll have to tell him I won't be going with him.'

'Oh, Lucy, pet. I'm sorry. . .' Charlotte sounded penitent now. 'I would have loved to see you. Do try to come up again for my birthday. . .that would be lovely. Avril would love it too.'

'I'll try, Mum. You have a nice bus tour. Love to Avril. Must fly.' She hung up with a sigh. And she wasn't sure whether she was sighing over missing out on seeing her mother or over what Charlotte had said about Case Travers. Or. . . She swallowed. Or was it because she was going to miss out on her drive up to Brisbane with Case?

Fool, she berated herself. Charlotte's right. Heaven knows where she heard those things, but she's right. Men like Case Travers are best avoided.

With another sigh, an even deeper one this time, she picked up the phone again and asked for the number of his room. But when she tried the number there was no answer.

Was he having a leisurely breakfast somewhere? Or an early-morning swim? She'd just have to meet him in the foyer at ten, as arranged, and tell him then.

She headed for the bathroom, ignoring—or trying to—a brief twinge of regret.

Just before ten she took a lift down to the main foyer. She spied Case at once, at the reception desk, in the process of checking out.

'Ah, you're bright and early.' He looked approving as he turned to face her. 'Looking very bright, I must say. . .not a sign of your late night.' The black eyes lingered a moment on her face before flicking away. 'Someone bringing down your luggage?' he asked, when he saw that she was empty-handed.

'Case, I tried to ring you in your room,' she said, her heart racing for some odd reason. 'I won't be coming with you.'

'You won't?' He frowned. 'You're saying your mother's still not at home? Look, if she and Avril have stayed overnight somewhere, they might still come home before the day's out—'

'Mum *is* at home.' Lucy finally got a word in. 'Or rather, she was when I rang earlier. But she was about to go away for a few days on a bus tour, leaving this morning. So there's not much point driving up to Brisbane to see her. She won't be there.'

'Ah.' He looked disappointed, she thought. Genuinely disappointed, his lips drawing inward almost in pique. Her heart gave a flutter.

'So. . .what do you intend to do?' He raised a whimsical eyebrow. 'Stay here at Surfers for the weekend?'

A weekend relaxing in the sun. . . It was tempting. But that would mean another night at this expensive five-star hotel. Her teeth tugged at her lip. It was still early morning. The whole day lay ahead. 'I'll try to get a flight back this evening,' she decided aloud, 'and spend the day on the beach.'

'You're in no hurry, then, to rush back to join your lover?' His tone gently mocked her.

Her cheeks burned. 'David and I are not joined at the hip,' she said tartly, hoping to stop any further questions about David.

'Or anywhere else, if you ask me. Let alone. . .the heart.' His eyes caught and challenged hers.

'Well, I'm not asking you.' She felt the heightened warmth in her cheeks as she wrenched her eyes away from his, transferring her gaze to his mouth instead. Her colour deepened as she found her eyes clinging in a kind of helpless fascination to his firm, well-shaped lips, and she imagined with a fluttery breath what that warm, sensual mouth would feel like coming down on hers.

She dropped her gaze abruptly.

'You're telling me it's none of my business.'

Not sure if she could trust her voice at that moment, she summoned a non-committal smile.

He leaned closer, forcing her to look at him again, making her acutely aware of the strong, sharp lines of his face. 'You're still not sure that you want him. . .are you?' he taunted softly. 'And if my eyes didn't deceive me last night, he has a few doubts of his own. It's hardly a grand passion. . .is it?'

Her eyes leapt to his. What had he seen? What did he know?

She compressed her lips and said nothing.

He didn't pursue it. 'Look, why not stay on here for the whole weekend? You're not booked to fly back until tomorrow night. Why change it? I'll let the airline know you'll be boarding from here, not Brisbane.'

'I don't think—'

'Stay on here as my guest,' he offered expansively. 'As Maxi Board's guest,' he amended as he saw her lips parting in protest.

She shook her head. 'Thank you, but I couldn't accept another night.' With David now virtually out of her life she could no longer claim any connection with Maxi Board. Not that Case Travers knew about that yet. . .and she had no intention of telling him. He just might get the idea that she'd broken it off because of *him*. 'In fact—'

'Not another word. We took extra rooms for the weekend, in case any of our people wanted to stay on. It's all taken care of. Just let them know at the desk that you'll be staying the extra night.'

All taken care of, was it? We'll see about that, Lucy thought, bristling at his high-handed manner. 'Please give me my air ticket,' she repeated firmly. 'I'd rather go back tonight.' She would ring the airline right away and change her flight to this evening. There was no way she was going to be obligated to Case Travers! Anyway, an evening spent on her own didn't appeal.

'As you wish.' With an indifferent shrug Case dug into the satchel he was carrying and pulled out her ticket. 'Allow me,' he said silkily. 'I'll make sure you get a good seat.'

'Thank you,' she said primly. 'It was kind of you to offer me a lift to Brisbane, Case,' she added with a polite smile. 'I appreciate it. I hope you have a good day. . .with your friends.' She felt a faint pang, and instantly stifled it.

'Ah, well, actually. . .' A lopsided smile dragged at his lips. 'My plans have changed slightly too. I've just spoken to my friends in Brisbane and they won't be there either. There's been a sudden death in the family and they need to rally round, spend time with their relatives.'

Her heart stopped. Was that true? Why did she get the feeling that he'd plucked the story from the air in the past couple of seconds?

'But I still intended to drive you to Brisbane,' he hastened to add, implying that a promise was a promise. 'However, since you now don't need to go and neither do I, well. . .why bother to drive up there?'

'You'll be flying home this morning?' The question slipped out. She hoped he couldn't see the way her heart was leaping about under the light top she was wearing over her white shorts.

'Um, I don't think so. I reckon a weekend relaxing here in the sun sounds far more tempting. Excuse me for a moment.' He pulled out a mobile phone and stabbed it with his finger, turning partially aside as he spoke into it. After a few short, sharp words he swung back to her, his expression darkly benign.

'Looks as if you'll have to stay the night after all, Lucy. The airlines have called a snap twenty-four-hour strike. We're stuck here until tomorrow. So it looks as if we'll both be flying back tomorrow evening as originally planned.'

Lucy's jaw dropped. He'd hardly lie about a thing like that, surely? No. . .now that she looked around the lobby, she realised it was true. People were pacing about with their luggage in tow, looking disgruntled, exasperated or downright furious. It was true. She was trapped here at Surfers. For the next twenty-four hours.

With Case Travers.

'I'll extend your room for another night, Lucy. Don't look so dismayed.' His eyes were mocking her now. 'You could be stuck in worse places. Surely a weekend in the sun is just what a sporty, outdoor girl like you should lap up? Swimming, sunbathing, browsing around the shops. . .'

She croaked agreement.

'And this evening. . .' The black eyes gleamed into hers, powerfully compelling, dangerously enticing. 'There's a new seafood place I've been told is a must. I'll take you there for dinner. Don't move!'

She watched dazedly as he stepped over to the desk and gave the girl a disarming smile. 'My plans have changed,' he informed her. 'I won't be checking out after all. This darned air strike! I'll be staying another night. And kindly extend Miss Farrell's room for another night too.'

Lucy was thankful his eyes were averted. It gave her a moment to snatch back the breath that had caught in her throat and get some control over her trembling body. Dinner? With Case Travers? Her mother's warnings tumbled back. Was he hoping to spend more than just the evening with her? The whole *night*, maybe? The trembling intensified.

'All fixed.' Case swung back. 'No problem with us staying another night. So. . .what are you planning to do first up, Lucy? Head for the shops? Or did you do that yesterday afternoon?'

'I went swimming yesterday.' She tilted her chin. Did he think all women were shopping-mad? 'And this morning I intend to do the same. Swimming. Sunbaking. Body-surfing.'

'Well, keep inside the flags. A shark grabbed someone along this coast a fortnight ago.' There was a sudden glint in his eye that struck Lucy as being highly predatory, as if he were imagining what a succulent meal *she* would make. She recalled what her mother had said about him devouring women, and she stiffened warily, her nerve-ends bristling.

'There's no need to worry,' he swept on, as if sensing her tension and putting it down to fear of sharks, 'if you stay within the patrolled area.'

'I will. Thanks for the warning.' A warning in more ways than one, she thought as she turned away, heading for the lifts.

'I might see you down on the beach,' he called after her.

'Maybe.' A tide of heat rose up her slender neck to colour her face, and she was relieved he couldn't see it.

Her thoughts as she made her escape were chaotic, a mixture of uncertainty, vague yearnings, a heady excitement and a deep vein of mistrust. Yet she had to

admit it. She did want to see him again. . .even as every
fibre of her being warned her against him. It was
madness, and she knew it. This was no ordinary man.
No safe, unthreatening member of her own circle. This
was Case Travers, the powerful, prosperous paperboard tycoon. The jaded, cynical ex-husband. The
suave philanderer who was rarely seen with the same
woman twice.

In his eyes, no doubt, she was a sitting target. A
lonely, vulnerable woman, uncertain of her feelings for
the man in her life, forced to stay alone for the weekend
in a romantic sub-tropical paradise—an idyllic setting
just made for seduction—and with, as far as he was
aware, a doting boyfriend back home who'd be there
to console her and pick up the pieces after he'd had his
wicked way with her.

She giggled a trifle hysterically as she rode up alone
in the lift. The strong Queensland sun must have gone
to her head already! Case Travers was David's *boss*,
for heaven's sake. By all reports a caring, considerate
boss, who looked out for his employees and the people
who were close to them. That was the only reason he
was putting himself out for her, offering to see her
again. He felt obligated.

But, in her heart of hearts, she wondered if she
believed it.

As she changed into a figure-hugging gold maillot,
pulled a long shirt over the top, then grabbed her
beachbag and towel, she sternly reminded herself that
Case Travers was a man who steamrollered and
manipulated people, who moved his victims around
like pieces on a chessboard, to dance to his bidding. . .
a man who made things happen the way he wanted
them to happen.

He might genuinely have been trying to reunite her
with David, but if her instincts meant anything at all he
hadn't been acting purely out of the goodness of his
heart. There was more to it. . .she would swear it.

Well, he would find that Lucy Farrell, the naïve little podiatrist from the suburbs, wouldn't be dancing to whatever tune he happened to be playing on *this* occasion!

Shouts rang out from the water, rising to shrieks as the swollen waves reared and broke, thundering onto the shore in a tumbling froth of white. The soft sand under Lucy's feet was dazzling white under the bright glare of the late May sun. Suntanned bodies lay everywhere.

She recognised a few faces from last night, but nobody approached her as she spread out her towel on the sand. After slapping on some suntan oil, she stretched out on her towel, face-down.

It was delicious feeling the sun's heat seeping into her bones, feeling her body relaxing and her cares slipping away. She wasn't sure how long she lay there, drinking in the sensuous warmth, before a familiar voice intruded.

'You haven't gone to sleep, I trust? You'll fry in this sun.'

She opened one eye and looked up, her heart thudding as she saw Case standing over her like a magnificent bronzed Adonis, clad only in brief black trunks, a colourful beachtowel slung over one shoulder. Somehow she managed to unlock her tongue. 'Not me. I remembered to slip, slap, slop.'

'Looks as if you could with some more. Want me to oblige?' As he reached down for her suntan oil she rolled over and sat up, her eyes widening in alarm.

'No need,' she said breathlessly. 'I'm about to go for a swim.' The sight of Case Travers' near-naked body, all firm bronzed flesh and smooth rippling muscle, was seductive enough without having his hands running over her own semi-naked body. Much as the thought of it sent her pulses spinning.

He paused, and straightened. 'You mean that little gold number isn't just for show?' His eyes seared over her, but she had the distinct feeling it wasn't her costume he was devouring with his gaze. Her exposed flesh, tanned to a deep golden honey over the long summer and autumn months, tingled under his scrutiny.

'Of course not,' she said, springing to her feet without assistance from the hand he thrust out. 'At home I go swimming every morning before work. So I need togs I know will be practical in the water. Why?' she challenged, her eyes mocking him. 'Do the women you mix with only come to the beach to be seen, not to get their bikinis or their immaculate hair-dos wet?'

His lips eased into a crooked, joltingly attractive smile. 'Let's just say I know a few who do. Right now I'd prefer to mix with a woman like you.'

'Would you, now?' she countered, to cover a ripple of nervousness—and unexpected pleasure, stifling for the moment her mother's warnings and her own simmering mistrust. She slanted a look at him. 'Do you make a habit of flirting with the female friends of your. . .subordinates?'

He squinted at her, the sunlight giving his narrowed eyes a brilliant glitter. Then he laughed—a brief, amused sound. 'For one thing, I'm not flirting. . .I'm stating a simple fact. For another, I don't look on my engineers—or any of my staff, for that matter—as subordinates. They're valued colleagues. . .equals. And for another, I'm still not convinced that you and my valued engineer-cum-acting plant manager are right for each other or truly care for each other, so I don't look on you as his. . .property. I look on you, Lucy, as an individual. . .a free spirit who can decide for herself who she spends her time with.'

Lucy's chin rose a notch. 'I said I was his *friend*, not his *property*. . .and never will be.'

She twisted away from him, heading for the water,

leaving deep imprints in the soft sand with each spirited stride.

He caught up with her. 'Good for you.' Amusement licked through his voice. 'I like an independent, free-thinking, strong-minded woman. I can see you're a woman who'll never be pressured into doing anything you don't want to do. Even if,' he taunted, 'you're also a woman who doesn't know her own mind when it comes to the man in her life.'

Her head snapped round. 'Isn't it better to be sure about someone before you rush headlong into a marriage you might regret?' she shot back. She caught her breath in dismay as she recalled his own short-lived marriage. 'Case, I—I'm sorry,' she faltered, her deep blue eyes contrite now. 'I wasn't. . .I didn't think. . .'

'No problem.' His mouth twisted. 'You're right. You'd be crazy to marry a guy you're not a hundred per cent sure about. *I* rushed headlong into matrimony. . .and lived to regret it. I won't make the same mistake twice.'

Meaning he didn't ever intend to marry again? Or didn't intend to marry again until he was a hundred per cent sure? Lucy flicked another look round at him as her feet struck the seething foam at the shoreline. Judging by the hard glitter in his eye and the cynical lines round his mouth, he'd sworn off love and marriage for good. Which she'd do well to keep in mind.

Hadn't her mother warned her? Hadn't her own common sense warned her to beware of him, right from the start?

Regardless of any warnings, she was laughing along with him as they both emerged, cool and refreshed, from the surf, snatching up their beachtowels to rub over their tingling, dripping bodies.

'That was great!' she burst out. When had she ever shared anything like this with David? He liked to swim occasionally—in a pool—but he hated the sea and especially hated the surf. Case, on the other hand, was a strong swimmer and a superb body-surfer, and she'd had fun matching him stroke for stroke, wave for wave. Few men *could* match her in the water.

Her heart gave a jump as Case glanced down at her. His thick dark hair was damply ruffled, falling over his tanned brow in moist spikes, giving him a more reckless, more carefree and if possible even more sexy image than the coolly sophisticated, sartorially elegant one he projected back home, as the stunningly successful businessman he was.

'How about we go back to the hotel, get dressed and then go for a drive?' Case suggested. 'My hire car's going begging. We could head for the mountains and find a place to have lunch.'

She only just managed not to blink. He wanted to spend the rest of his day with her? As well as dinner this evening?

'Sure. . .OK,' she said lightly, if rather unsteadily, burying her head in her towel and rubbing vigorously to blot out the sudden image of her mother's despairing face. I know the kind of man he is, Mum. I'll be careful, she promised silently.

They drove inland to the spectacularly beautiful Lamington National Park, lunching in cool comfort at the Binna Burra Mountain Lodge to the shrill cacophony of bird sounds. Before driving on, Lucy suggested a leisurely bush walk into the surrounding rainforest, her eyes challenging him. He accepted the challenge without turning a hair.

'You must be sorry you missed your mother today,' he commiserated as they lapped up the fresh clean air and the wild, lush beauty around them. 'Only just missed her, by the sound of it. She must have been disappointed.' He seemed to pause, before asking lazily, 'Did she know you were intending to drive up with me? Or did she think you'd be driving up with David?'

She glanced up at him. Was he trying to find out what her mother thought of David? Or what her mother thought of *him*? Why would he *care*?

'I told her that David had had to go back to Melbourne and that you'd offered me a lift. Why do you ask?' The question was out before she thought twice.

After another brief pause he answered lightly, 'No particular reason.' He caught her eye, saw her blush, and added smoothly, a mocking gleam in the dark depths of his eyes, 'Mothers tend not to trust me with their daughters. A totally unfounded mistrust, I assure you. The women I've taken up with have normally cut the apron strings long before they come into my orbit.'

Meaning he wasn't interested in *her* that way?

She took a deep breath. 'Well, you. . .do have something of a reputation,' she challenged.

'Do I?' He laughed. But it lacked the amusement she'd expected. It held more of a derisive ring. 'So.' He lifted an eyebrow. 'She warned you not to have anything to do with me, did she?'

'No!' Her blush deepened at the quick denial. She was a hopeless liar. 'Well. . .yes, I suppose she did, in a way,' she admitted weakly. 'You—you know what mothers can be like. You only have to accept a lift from a man and they jump to all kinds of stupid conclusions.'

'I'll just have to meet your mother some time and restore my reputation,' Case said silkily, and changed the subject before she had time to catch her breath.

He didn't mean it, of course. Men like Case Travers didn't care about their reputations. Or about what mothers thought of them. He was probably secretly laughing his head off at both of them.

They drove back to Surfers to a blazing sunset, with just time to freshen up and change before leaving again for dinner.

The beachfront seafood restaurant Case had chosen was a couple of kilometres away by car, and on the way there Lucy wondered if Case had invited anyone else to join them. A number of Maxi Board people had stayed on at Surfers for the weekend, and Case hadn't exactly said they'd be alone.

When they were led to a small table for two she gulped in a lungful of air before sitting down, realising that it was only going to be the two of them. There was nobody else there that they knew. She wondered if Case was relieved about that. Or didn't he care if people saw them together? Most likely not. He'd made it clear that he looked on her as a free spirit, not as David's. . .property. As far as he was concerned, they were both free to do as they pleased, to see anyone they wished.

But why would he *want* to spend his time with her? He'd hinted that he felt responsible for her while she was here, since he was the one who'd persuaded her to come. But was that all it was?

She ran her tongue over her lips. With Case Travers' reputation for meaningless fly-by-night affairs, would he succumb to temptation—assuming he *was* tempted—and try to take advantage of the situation?

She flushed at the thought. If he did have seduction in mind, would she be strong enough, determined enough, to resist him? She let her breath whisper out in a sigh. She would just have to be! She'd never believed in casual affairs with no deep feeling involved—let alone meaningless one-night stands—and she didn't intend to give in now, no matter how tempted she might be.

Over their exquisitely succulent lobster salads, Case gave no sign, no hint that he was planning to entice her into his bed later in the evening. He didn't overdo the wine. He didn't gaze into her eyes with lecherous intent. There was nothing suggestive in his tone or his comments. He was attentive, charming and fascinating to talk to. In fact, they talked about just about every-thing under the sun, only in the latter stages of the evening touching on anything personal, when he asked lightly, 'You've lived in Melbourne all your life?'

'Only from the age of ten,' she told him. 'I was born in Sydney. My mother's Melbourne-born, but moved to Sydney in her twenties, met my father there and later came back to Melbourne when his bank trans-ferred him from Sydney.'

'Ah.' Case nodded. 'Funny how fate works, isn't it? If your mother hadn't moved to Sydney in her twenties, she might never have met your father. Or had you.' His eyes lingered on hers for a second, before he asked, 'What prompted your mother to leave Melbourne in the first place?' His brow quirked. 'Escaping an unhappy love affair?'

Lucy gave a shrug, reeling slightly from the impact of that dark gaze. 'Maybe.' She'd often wondered. Her mother had never talked much about that period of her life. She'd always been oddly unresponsive, evasive, even, when quizzed in any depth. 'She's never said. Just that she got tired of her job and left.'

Case toyed with his coffee-cup. 'Maybe she was having some personal hassles—perhaps at work? Someone harassing her, do you think?'

'She's never mentioned any problems at work. I think she just wanted a change of scene. . .that's all she's ever said.'

'What line of work was she in? Was it in the city?'

'Somewhere in the city, I think. She had a job as a cost accountant. I'm not sure where. Some finance company, I think.' Lucy was surprised at his interest in her mother. Or was it just to keep the conversation rolling? 'She has a degree in commerce and accounting. She's always been a whizz in that area. . .unlike me.'

Case's lips were pursed, as if he found it strange that she knew so little detail about that time in her mother's life. 'She found similar work in Sydney?'

'Still in finance...yes. But in public hospitals, not in the business world. By the time she met my father she was finance manager of her hospital. Dad was a bank accountant in those days, and did some hospital auditing in his spare time.' She took a brief sip of coffee. 'They married a few years later. By the time Dad's bank transferred us to Melbourne he was a branch bank manager. I was ten, as I said, and my brother two years older.'

'Your mother was happy to come back to Melbourne?'

She glanced at Case over the rim of her cup. She was beginning to wonder if there was something behind all these questions about her mother. Something more than a polite interest. She frowned. Was he checking out her background to see if she was *worthy* of his interest, his time? Background, she thought with a derisive curl of her lip, was often all-important to people with impeccable, silver-studded pedigrees.

Swallowing a rush of indignation mingled with a vague disappointment, she tried to answer normally. 'I don't think she was too happy about it, actually. She always complained that she found Melbourne too cold and damp in the winter. That was one of the reasons she decided to move up to Queensland a year or so ago. And for her friend Avril's sake too, of course. It wasn't as if...' Her eyes clouded briefly. 'As if she had a husband to keep her in Melbourne.'

'The divorce must have come as a severe blow to you and your brother.' Case sounded genuinely concerned, and she wondered if she had misjudged him. 'I know my father suffered terribly when his own parents—my grandparents—split up. In those days it was even harder than it is today, divorce being so rare then. It's toughest on the children, Dad always said.'

She seized her chance to switch the focus back on him. 'Your father must have been grateful, then, that

you and your wife split up before *you* had any children,'
she ventured.

She sensed his withdrawal, saw his face harden, his
eyes grow cold.

'There wasn't much chance of that happening. My
wife didn't want children. Unfortunately, she chose not
to tell me until after we were married.' His voice was
toneless, masking any pain or anger that might still
linger. 'She let me believe that she did. . .that she loved
kids.'

'Oh!' She looked at him in shock. 'How terrible for
you. And you did want them. . .obviously.'

'Why else does one choose to get married?' he said,
a wealth of disillusionment and cynicism in his voice.

'I've always believed,' she heard herself blurting
involuntarily, 'that if you love someone deeply enough,
you want to marry them and live with them for the rest
of your life. . .and that any children who come are an
added bonus.'

'Ah. . .an old-fashioned romantic,' he mocked. She
half expected him to add, How quaint, but instead, he
raised a finger for the bill and said abruptly, 'Guess
we'd better be heading back. . .it's getting late.'

They stuck to trivialities on the drive back to the
hotel, and Lucy was surprised when their lift reached
her floor and Case, instead of bidding her goodnight,
insisted on seeing her to her room. By the time they
arrived at her door she was feeling quite breathless,
her heart beating a wild tattoo in her chest. Was he
hoping she would invite him in? Would he *insist* on
coming in, expecting a reward—or his *due*, more
likely—for all the attentions he'd lavished on her, the
money he'd spent on her?

Even as her pulses raced at the thought she felt a
vague pang that he should see her in that light. . .as just
another easy female—one of many since his divorce—
willing and ready for a casual one-night fling. She no

doubt struck him, in her emotionally mixed-up state, as being more susceptible than most.

No way, José, she thought, wishing she could ignore the urgings of her body, which were weakening her resolve and tempting her to give in to whatever erotic pleasures he might have in mind.

As she burrowed into her handbag for her pass-key, feeling all fingers and thumbs, Case said coolly, 'I won't come in...assuming you were going to offer me a nightcap.' His eyes challenged hers as she glanced up at him. 'We wouldn't want anyone catching me emerging from the room of such a respectable young lady this late at night,' he said smoothly, 'and ruining her reputation.'

Or *yours*, she thought, as relief mingled with a treacherous ache of regret whirled through her. Maybe he wasn't the out-and-out rake she'd imagined him to be. Or was he thinking of David, who, after all, held a senior position in his company? Case Travers was known to care about the people who worked for him. And David was, as far as Case knew, still in the picture, still a part of her life—scathing as he might be about their relationship, their compatibility, their feelings for each other. 'Hardly a grand passion,' as he'd put it.

'How thoughtful of you,' she said, matching his smooth tone with an effort. 'In that case I won't invite you in.' The very thought set her body quivering again, heat swirling through her.

'Thank you for making my day such an unexpectedly pleasant one, Lucy,' Case said formally. 'I hope it's helped to quell your disappointment at not seeing your mother?'

Was *that* why he'd spent his day with her? To soften her disappointment? Nothing personal after all? No hidden agenda? The thought helped her to get a better control over her turbulent emotions.

'It has.' She gave him a quick smile. 'It's been a lovely day for me too.' And it had, surprisingly. Worlds apart they might be, in so many ways, but Case was good company—charming, exciting, intoxicating company. She ought to be thankful he hadn't tried to seduce her into an ignominious one-night stand. It showed he must have some respect for her.

But was respect all she wanted from him? an insidious voice niggled.

'Well. . .goodnight, Lucy.' He set her pulses leaping again by trailing a finger down the slender curve of her throat. 'Such a lovely neck. A neck made for adornment,' he murmured. 'And yet. . .you always leave it bare.'

The touch of his warm fingerip on her skin was sending shivers down her spine, threatening to strangle the breath in her throat. She swallowed—hard.

'I look ridiculous cluttered up with jewellery,' she said, finding her voice. 'I have a couple of gold and silver chains I wear at times, but I tend to lose them at swimming pools or gyms,' she confided with a quick, nervous laugh. 'Anyway—' she shrugged '—jewellery is just not for me.'

'Not heavy, garish jewellery or cheap trinkets. . . perhaps not. But a fine piece for the evening—an exquisite piece of the finest, most delicate quality—to adorn this graceful neck. . .' His hand brushed over her nape, his fingers sliding through the silkiness of her hair. More shivers whispered through her as his hand curled round the back of her neck. 'But I'm embarrassing you.' He gave a soft, throaty chuckle. 'I must go. Goodnight, Lucy.'

And then—holding her thus captive—he bent his head and kissed her.

It was so unexpected she barely had time to catch her breath. The touch of his lips on hers was electrifying. She felt her body tingling, melting, felt her lips softening under the sensual pressure of his, her senses leaping vividly to life in a way she couldn't recall ever happening before, not like this. Involuntarily she opened her mouth and moved her lips, almost experimentally, under his. She wanted the kiss to last. . . longed to feel more of the spine-tingling sensations rioting through her.

But it ended as abruptly as it had begun.

She heard a sharp intake of breath as he drew back, and wasn't sure if the sound came from him or herself. His eyes flared, glittering darkly, their inky blackness burning into her own as he looked down at her. She had the wildest feeling that he was fighting the temptation to drag her back into his arms and kiss her senseless.

She wouldn't have stopped him. She couldn't have, even if she'd wanted to. Her body felt paralysed, beyond her control. As it was, her swollen lips parted instinctively, and she felt her eyes drowning helplessly in the shimmering darkness of his.

'Don't tempt me,' he gritted through clenched teeth. 'I wouldn't be responsible. . .' He stepped back abruptly. 'See you in the morning, Lucy.'

He was gone before she could unlock her frozen tongue to utter a word, before she could even blink. It was only when she heard the *ding* of the lift that she came to life and stumbled, shaking, into her room.

CHAPTER SIX

CASE was the first person she saw when she came down to breakfast the next morning. He was with a middle-aged couple Lucy vaguely recalled having seen at the dinner dance. As Case beckoned her over she found herself trying not to blush, her hands clammy.

'Join us, Lucy.' Rising, Case introduced the other couple as Marge and Larry Chambers. Larry, it seemed, was a paper merchant from Sydney. 'Lucy flew up from Melbourne to visit her mother,' Case told them easily, making no mention of the fact that her mother had gone away. 'She's grabbed the chance to catch up with some of her Maxi Board friends.'

Friends, *plural*, Lucy noted. Making it clear that she wasn't here alone with *him*! Protecting her reputation again. Or *his*. Or was he thinking of David, who worked for him?

The Sydney couple were already on their coffee and about to leave. 'Nice to have met you, Lucy,' they said as they excused themselves. 'Have a good day. You too, Case.'

Lucy, left alone with Case, found herself trembling like a nervous schoolgirl. Annoyed with herself, she bent her head over her bowl of muesli, gripping her spoon like a lifeline.

'Your hair's wet,' Case commented. 'Been swimming already?'

She glanced up. 'Only in the hotel pool. A few laps before breakfast.' She went on hastily, not wanting him to get the idea that she expected anything more of him, 'I'm going to take a bus trip to Seaworld later this morning, after a sunbake and a dip in the surf.'

'Forget the bus.' Case was dismissive. 'I'll drive you there. I still have the hire car.'

She drew in a quick breath, her heart missing a beat. 'You're saying—*you* want to go to Seaworld?' She slanted a look at him, her eyes sceptical.

'Why not? Performing dolphins. Death-defying roller-coaster rides. Sounds fun. I haven't had much clean, wholesome fun lately, I'm beginning to realise.'

No... Your type of fun would be more sophisticated, Lucy reflected with an ironic smile. Beautiful women, glamorous first nights, first-class travel...that kind of thing. Simple pursuits like body-surfing, brisk bush walks and performing dolphins might seem like a refreshing change for an enforced rest weekend. But it'll be a flash in the pan, I'll bet. Like I'll be a flash in the pan too. You'll be glad to get back to your pampered, high-powered world. And to your glitzy bimbos, with their more sophisticated demands.

'Mind if I share the joke?' Case asked, catching the smile on her lips.

She gave a quick laugh and shook her head. 'I think you'd rather not know,' she said.

'Oh?' His eyes taunted her. 'You think performing dolphins are not my cup of tea...is that it?'

'Close,' she admitted. Performing *females* would be more his style.

'Then I'll prove you wrong. I will enjoy it. I'm already enjoying this weekend enormously. Thanks to you. You're helping me to loosen up, have a bit of fun...something I haven't been doing enough of lately. It's doing wonders for me.' His dark gaze caught hers, something in the compelling depths shaking her to the core.

She let her eyelashes flutter down to hide a stab of pleasure—and some more powerful emotion, a reaction to that look in his eye. Yet her niggling mistrust still lingered. Could she believe a word he said?

'I'm glad you're finding your weekend therapeutic,'

she said lightly, aware of the heat in her cheeks and hoping it wasn't too noticeable.

'Oh, it's more than therapeutic,' he assured her, and she was faintly puzzled by a new note in his voice, a regretful, almost brooding note. As if he was thinking of something else now...something that caused him pain.

His ex-wife?

Or was he regretting what he'd said a moment ago, regretting that burning look he'd given her, that impulsive kiss last night? He'd shown then that he wasn't interested in a one-night stand, in adding her to his list of fly-by-night sexual conquests. He'd hardly want to risk getting *emotionally* involved with her, still less want *her* getting emotional about *him*, and becoming a nuisance to him.

Despite his slight withdrawal and her own qualms, they did have fun at Seaworld, licking ice-creams as they watched the antics of the whales and sea lions, and chuckling at the dolphins' flamboyant tricks. They took a heart-stopping ride on the triple-loop corkscrew roller-coaster, and afterwards, munching hot dogs, watched the acrobatic waterskiers.

It was a sweltering hot day, and Lucy had worn shorts and a brief top to Seaworld. Case had surprised her by turning up in shorts too, and a loose casual shirt. She couldn't imagine them being part of his normal suave wardrobe, and suspected he must have bought them while she was down on the beach earlier.

But he seemed perfectly at ease wearing them, just as he seemed perfectly at ease watching the dolphins and whales and sharing rides with squealing kids. She kept half expecting him to pull out a mobile phone, or to keep glancing at his watch, or to show his boredom in some other way, but he didn't.

Instinct told her he hadn't always been the jaded, cynical, hard-headed businessman he was today.

Maybe, before his marriage, he'd been more like this. . . more human, more relaxed, more down-to-earth. . . more fun. It was a pity he didn't let his hair down more often. Why, she wondered, had he chosen to let it down today?

All too soon they were on their way back to Surfers, Case flicking on the radio to flood the car with music.

'Want to browse around the shops before we check out and head for the airport?' he asked as they came in sight of Surfers' familiar high-rise skyline. 'You'll have an hour or so.'

She shook her head. 'I'd rather make the most of the sun and have a last dip in the surf and a jog along the beach.'

'You really are a fitness freak, aren't you?' Case said, and she glanced round at him, wondering if it was meant as a criticism.

Of course, Case Travers preferred women who were more feminine and sophisticated in their tastes. The well-bred, glamorous type, who moved in the exalted circles he did. The type who'd rather lounge around the pool all day, displaying their bikini-clad bodies and their bottled suntans. The type who liked buying up big in the chic fashion boutiques and sipping cocktails in the hotel bar. Which was probably what Case was dying to do right now. Without having her hanging around, preventing him from chatting up someone more to his taste.

'Why don't we just meet up in the hotel foyer in an hour's time?' she suggested as he swung the hire car into the hotel car park. 'Or meet at the airport?'

'Trying to get rid of me, are you?' He flicked a teasing look at her. 'Sick of my company already?'

'No. Of course not.' Was he implying that he wanted *hers*?

'Then in that case I'll join you for a swim and a jog,' he said coolly. 'You'll make a fit man of me yet.'

She jutted her chin, her natural frankness and sense

of humour drawing a wry retort. 'I failed with David. Why should I succeed with you?'

'Because I'm not David,' he said, and the way he said it made her heart skip a beat.

He didn't think that she and David were suited; he'd made that quite plain from the start. But was he also saying—implying—that he was interested in her himself? He'd just spent his entire weekend with her, and they'd had fun, but...

Get real, Lucy, she told herself. This is just an enforced holiday weekend to him. People act differently, out of character, when they're away from home with time on their hands, especially in a balmy subtropical setting like this. Face it. You won't see or hear from him again after this weekend.

And that would be the best thing that could happen. Because back home they belonged to different worlds. And the charismatic, super-successful Case Travers was light years away from her.

Your clock has just struck midnight, Cinderella, she mused with a sigh. It's back to rags for you, my girl. Goodbye, sweet prince... Goodbye, dreamworld... Back to the cold, hard, *real* world.

She threw herself back into her work with a vengeance, nigglingly aware of an empty ache inside her, as if something was missing from her life. Of course, David was missing from it...but she knew it wasn't David she was missing. It was a pair of night-dark eyes above smiling, sensuous lips...

Damn Case Travers, she thought fiercely. He'd spoilt her for any other man! Having known him, even for so brief a time, she knew in her heart that no other man would ever compare, would ever brighten up her life the way he had, would ever awaken the feelings he'd aroused in her...feelings that David had never been capable of stirring—even half as much.

Silly, romantic fool, she derided herself. Case hadn't

even bothered to say, See you again, when he'd put her into a taxi at Melbourne airport after their flight back from Surfers, simply thanking her for her company at the weekend before being whisked away by the head office limo which had come to pick him up.

What had she expected, for heaven's sake?

She wasn't interested anyway. He was spoilt, arrogant, womanising, domineering, manipulating. . . Every savage label she could think of rolled through her fevered mind, until she realised she was still thinking about him and threw up her hands in disgust.

On the Thursday after she got home from Surfers her phone rang, late at night. She snatched it up, her heart rolling over, as it had, stupidly, every time it had rung since she'd been back.

'Lucy? It's me. . .David. Don't hang up on me!'

She took a deep breath and released it before answering. 'I'm not going to hang up on you, David. Don't be silly.'

'Sorry. I know you wouldn't.' David sounded different somehow. Excited? Nervous? 'Er. . .how are you?' he asked.

'Fine. . .just fine,' she said cautiously. 'And you?'

'I'm fine too.' He *was* excited about something. She could hear it in his voice. 'Lucy, I. . .I've something to tell you.'

'Yes?' He'd finished restoring his vintage Delage, was that it? Few other things got him as excited as his cars.

'I've been promoted! To plant manager. Um. . .but not here in Melbourne. I'll be managing Maxi Board's corrugated box plant in Sydney!'

'Oh, David, congratulations! You mean you'll be moving to Sydney? To *live*?' He *had* shocked her. David had always hated change, hated any disruption to his life. He'd always seemed so settled and contented here in Melbourne, with his cars and his modest flat built on the same block of land as his old family home, where his parents still lived.

'You're saying you'll miss me?' She heard the doubt in his voice.

'Of course I'll miss you, David. Just because we're not—not—'

'You'll miss me as you'd miss a. . .good friend,' David said flatly. 'Not a lover. Not a man you'd ever intend to marry.' He sounded more accepting than bitter.

'No,' she agreed soberly, wanting to be honest with him. She was sure now that they'd done the right thing by splitting up when they had. She'd been sure, she realised, for some time. David was not the man for her. . .and never would be. It would be wrong—cruel—to dangle even a dim hope. She had to finish it here and now, once and for all. Even though it meant she'd be left with no one, with nothing—not even David's friendship, now that he was going away. . .for good.

'I wish you the very best, David,' she said sincerely. 'Plant manager! It's what you've always wanted. When do you go?'

'Tomorrow. It's all been rather sudden. The guy I'm replacing has been promoted to head office and they want me to start straight away. So the job's there for me now and I want to get started. Lu, it's a huge step up for me. I can't wait.'

'Tomorrow!' It certainly had come about very suddenly. And Case Travers, as owner and managing director of Maxi Board, had to be behind it.

Lucy pursed her lips, her heartbeat quickening. Would David's transfer to another state have come about if she and Case had never met? Her brow furrowed, a feeling close to outrage stirring inside her. She'd seen evidence before that Case Travers could be manipulative, steamrollering people and setting up situations to suit his own ends. But something like this. . . He couldn't have. . .wouldn't have. . .would he? To get David out of the way?

'I think your foot should feel much better now, Mrs Robb.' Lucy straightened, relieved that this was her last appointment before lunch. She was ready for a break. There had been a steady stream of minor problems, some irritatingly trivial, all morning. For some reason her work since she'd been back hadn't been giving her the same satisfaction as before. Her mind kept wandering. . .even more so since David's phone call last night.

'Excuse me, Lucy. . .' Holly, her young receptionist, poked her head round the door. 'Could you fit in one more patient before you go to lunch? Someone's just come in with an urgent problem. . .or so he says.'

Lucy nodded. 'Sure.' She never turned away an urgent case. Though in this case Holly sounded a bit sceptical, she thought. Some people did exaggerate their problems so they could get in without an appointment. 'Who is it?' she asked.

'He didn't give his name. He hasn't been before, he says. According to him, it's a small problem and shouldn't take long.'

'I thought you said it was urgent?'

'Small but urgent,' Holly asserted, reddening. She looked a bit flustered now. This guy has conned her, Lucy thought with a wry smile. He must be young and good-looking. Holly was highly susceptible to a handsome face.

'OK.' She sighed. 'Send him in. Mrs Robb is just leaving.' Lucy turned back to the old woman with a smile. 'I'd like to check your toe again in a month's time, Mrs Robb, all right?'

'All right, dear. And thank you. It's feeling much better already.' The old lady shuffled out with Holly's support.

Lucy just had time to clean up the room before Holly ushered in her new patient.

'Mr Travers,' Holly announced from the doorway.

Lucy swung round to find her gaze trapped by a pair of glittering black eyes. Her breath caught in her lungs.

Case! Case Travers as she had first seen him, suave and businesslike in an elegant charcoal suit, pristine white shirt and expensive silk tie. His crisp dark hair, which had been damp and windblown the last time she'd seen him, was now neatly brushed to one side, not a hair out of place, giving Lucy the poignant feeling that the casual, windswept Case Travers had been nothing but a dream, an illusion. A Cinderella fantasy.

'Thank you for seeing me,' Case said before she could find her voice. He flashed Holly a disarming smile. 'And thank *you*.'

Holly, flushing fiercely, came to life, mumbling, 'My pleasure,' as she hurriedly backed out. Summarily dismissed, Lucy thought with a droll smile.

'What have you done to my receptionist?' she demanded, deciding that attack—banter—was the best way to deal with the situation. Anything to cover her heart's frantic pounding.

'Done?' Case lifted a dark eyebrow. 'Nothing.' He glanced in the direction of the reclining chair. 'Is this where you like your patients to sit?'

'By all means,' she invited, gulping air into her lungs. 'Make yourself comfortable. You'd better take your shoes off first. You have. . .some urgent problem, I understand?' He wasn't limping. He didn't appear to be in any pain. In fact he looked in bronzed, virile, ravishing good health. No wonder Holly had been sceptical.

The black eyes flickered under hers. 'A small white lie, I confess. The urgency was. . .it's nearly lunchtime and I was hoping—'

'You're saying you're not here as a patient at all?'

Her eyes flashed turquoise sparks but underneath her pulses were skittering, careering out of control. She forced up her chin, assuming a steely demeanour. He wasn't going to get away with this. . .whatever he had in mind! 'My receptionist has booked you in as a bona fide patient, and as such—'

'Ah, but I am a bona fide patient,' he assured her equably. 'The urgency was that I wanted to catch you before you went to lunch. I shall pay for any. . .services you provide. Naturally.'

She swallowed. What 'services' did he require, precisely?

'What's wrong with you?' she asked suspiciously.

'Stress,' came the grave response. 'I need some stress-relief. Perhaps. . .a brief foot massage?'

She gasped. Was he serious? 'I don't do massage,' she said levelly. 'You'll have to go to a masseur. . .or a *masseuse*.' That would be more your style, she thought derisively.

'Ah,' he said. 'Well, in that case, there's no point taking off my shoes. Or even sitting down in your comfortable chair. End of consultation. Are you free for lunch?'

She caught her breath again. This man was incorrigible! 'Why do you ask?' she countered, determined not to jump at his command, as he obviously expected her to, but knowing in her heart that even if she hadn't been free she would have tried to arrange it. . .somehow.

His mouth eased into the dazzlingly attractive, lop-sided smile that had been haunting her dreams all week. 'Because I'd like to take you out to lunch. . .if you'll come,' he added with mock humility. 'I have a business proposition to put to you,' he slid in before she could answer. 'How long do you have?'

'I've finished here for the day but I'm giving a lecture at a sports clinic at three,' she admitted, her heart dipping a little. A business proposition? It wasn't a social lunch, then, merely for the pleasure of her company. Well, of course not.

'Then we've plenty of time.' Magnetic dark eyes caught and held hers. 'You'll come?'

Her heart gave a ridiculous jolt. 'OK. Thanks,' she said airily, adding as she waved him through the door, 'I'll meet you outside in five minutes. There'll be no charge,' she told him, relenting, a mocking smile curving her lips.

'Oh, but I insist on paying your consulting fee.' He tossed her a grin. 'You go and freshen up your lipstick, or whatever you have to do. I'll be waiting outside at my car. . .after settling my debts.'

Case Travers had spoken.

His car, she saw when she came out, was a business-like grey BMW. She had half-expected to see something more flashy—a slinky, eye-catching sports model, or even a super-luxurious Rolls or Bentley. Case was obviously sure enough of himself not to need such showy trappings to bolster his ego and flaunt his wealth.

He took her to an Italian restaurant in a nearby suburb, one she'd never been to. It was extremely elegant—and pricey too, she didn't doubt—and she was glad she'd worn an attractive cream blouse and slim skirt to work today, rather than the tailored trousers and plain sweater she sometimes wore.

Over their pumpkin ravioli starters, she reminded him briskly, 'You mentioned a business proposition.' If this was a business lunch, they might as well get down to business.

'That's right, I did.' He reached out to top up her glass of chablis before elaborating. 'Actually, you were the one who put the idea into my head,' he told her, making her wonder what on earth could be coming. 'I'm surprised I never considered it before myself. Too busy, I guess, with profits and balance sheets and grandiose money-making schemes. Concentrating on the company rather than the people who run it for me. Losing sight of the whole picture. The human element.'

What *was* he talking about? She stared at him, mystified. 'What. . .whole picture?' she ventured.

He spread his hands. 'Last weekend—' did his eyes soften as he said it? '—made me look at my priorities. Or what ought to be my priorities. Health. . .exercise. . . fitness. These things haven't been high on my agenda—or my company's agenda—to date. Yet fit, healthy, stimulated employees are the key to a fit, healthy, stimulated company, don't you agree?

'My people at head office—in marketing, administration, sales, computing—work long hours and get little or no exercise during that time, and they don't have time in their breaks to go out seeking running tracks or gyms elsewhere. So I've decided to install a gymnasium in the building, within easy reach of all.' He paused for her reaction.

'Good for you.' She smiled her approval. 'That's a great idea.' But where did she fit in?

'I'm glad you think so. Being into sport and fitness, you know about gyms. You go to a gym regularly, you told me, and you once worked as a part-time gym instructor. Well, now. . .' His eyes pinned hers, the black depths swallowing her riveted gaze. 'I want you to be my consultant, Lucy. My chief adviser.

'I want you to work with the builder I'm bringing in to convert one floor of our head office building into a gym. And with me too, of course. We'll have regular meetings during the planning stages. Will you do it?' His dark eyebrows shot up. 'You can choose your own time, day or evening. Or at weekends, if that suits you better. You'll have a free hand. And you'll be paid generously. . .naturally.'

Her lips parted. 'Regular meetings. . .evenings. . . weekends. . .' The words, and the images they conjured up, whirled through her mind, leaving her dizzy.

It's a business proposition. . .purely that, the more

realistic voice of caution reminded her. This must be why Case Travers had paid her so much attention at Surfers. The idea must have been in his mind then.

Even as she bristled at the realisation she was thinking, Why shouldn't I do it? The idea excited her. It would be an interesting change, a stimulating new challenge. And now that the triathlon season had finished for the winter and David was out of her life, she had more spare time. . .

She cleared her throat. 'I'd like to. . .very much. If you think I'm qualified enough to do it. *I* think I could do it,' she asserted. In business, she reflected, you have to be confident of your own ability. And this is business. Maxi Board is *big* business.

Exciting as it sounded, she paused to wonder if the real reason she'd accepted so readily was the thought of seeing more of Case Travers. A stupidly naïve and dangerous incentive! What if Case guessed? He'd either pity her secretly or get rid of her quick smart! And that would be mortifying!

On the other hand. . . What if Case himself had some hidden agenda? She bit her lip, remembering her mother's warnings about him, about the way he picked up and dicarded women. If Case Travers imagined for a minute that this would be a good opportunity to pick up and later discard *her*, he could jolly well think again! She wouldn't mind being picked *up*—the very thought made her nerve-ends tingle from head to toe—but not if it meant being tossed aside the moment he tired of his little fling with her and wanted a new fling with somebody else!

No. If Case Travers had any hanky-panky in mind, he'd soon find out that this was one girl who had no intention of playing the frivolous bedroom games *he* liked to play. No sirree. She already felt too. . .too. . .

But she mustn't even think it!

She would try, she decided, to hold their meetings during working hours, leaving the evenings and weekends free for her own private research on the subject. She would feel a lot more in control. And a whole lot safer!

They discussed the proposed gym for a while, then, having exhausted the subject, Case sat back, remarking in a silken drawl, 'You haven't mentioned David, Lucy. Seen much of him since you've been back?'

Her blue eyes glinted, quick resentment flaring at the way he'd coolly, clinically reorganised David's life. 'You must know David's been busy preparing for his move to Sydney. I assume that was your idea, was it?' Before she could stop herself she blurted out, 'You thought I couldn't make up my mind about him, so you decided you'd make it up for me. . .was that it?'

She flushed furiously, appalled at herself for openly accusing him of something so blatantly manipulative, for even thinking it. Why would Case Travers want to interfere in *her* life? She was nothing to him. 'I—I'm sorry,' she gasped. 'That was. . .unforgivable. And stupid.'

He shocked her by admitting blandly, 'No. You're quite right. I *was* the one who put the offer to David, knowing he'd be the best man for the job. And David, I might add, jumped at the chance. He made it quite plain he *wanted* to go.' His eyes narrowed, a dark speculative gleam in the piercing black. 'And *has* it helped you make up your mind? Are you planning to follow him to Sydney?'

With an effort, she eyed him coolly, her heart doing a slow, swinging loop inside her. He must know she had no intention of following him, or she wouldn't have accepted this consultancy job. Her heart stopped in mid-beat. Was that why he'd offered it to her? To make sure she didn't?

She drew in an unsteady breath. This man, she thought, is not only manipulative, but ruthless! But. . . why would he want to break us up?

Before she could take the thought any further, his voice ground out, 'What the hell's going on between you two? When I asked David if he'd be prepared to go up to Sydney straight away, he said yes on the spot. When I asked him how *you'd* feel about it, he said you'd probably be relieved to see him go. But you don't look relieved to me. You look thoroughly put out.' His brow plunged. '*Are* you thinking of following him to Sydney?'

Was he concerned about the work on the gym he'd asked her to do for him? Or. . . She swallowed, cutting dead the half-formed thought and forcing an answer. 'No. . .I won't be following him.'

'Then moving him to Sydney *did* help you make up your mind?' Case said, his eyes glinting now with mocking satisfaction.

She gave an infuriated toss of her head. He was so sure of himself! 'I didn't need any help making up my mind. Yours or anyone else's,' she bit out. 'We'd parted company *before* David heard he was going to Sydney. Well before. I haven't see him since I've been back from Surfers; I've only spoken to him on the phone. In fact, we agreed to—to part while we were up at Surfers.' There! she thought, her eyes taunting him. I can make up my mind without your help, Case Travers!

His black eyes flared, then narrowed. 'You broke it off up at *Surfers*? And you never told me? Why didn't you?'

She gave a shrug and dropped her gaze, examining the wine in her glass as if she found its colour fascinating. 'I didn't think it was any of your business,' she said coolly. More coolly than she felt.

She almost jumped out of her skin as she felt his hand touch hers and close over it. 'You're a mighty unusual woman, Lucy Farrell. I wonder if I'll ever fully understand you. Or ever. . .outguess you.' His tone was whimsical now, lacking the cynicism that was so often there. 'One thing I do know. I'm going to have a hell of a time finding out.'

Her head jerked up. And what she saw glittering in

the black depths of his eyes this time sent prickly waves all the way down her body.

At the same time she had a vision of her mother's disapproving face.

Lucy blinked, deliberately blotting out the image.

CHAPTER SEVEN

THE plans for Maxi Board's head office gym were well under way. Lucy had had several meetings with the builder already, to discuss the floor plan and equipment, after doing some initial research herself—not only at her own gym but at other gyms around town to gather up-to-the-minute ideas.

Case sat in on most of their meetings, which they held on the floor he wanted converted into a gym. It was a huge space he'd given her to work on, and Lucy was excited at the scope it offered her. It meant there was more than enough room for all the equipment she felt necessary, as well as shower rooms, toilets, changing rooms and a small first-aid room.

On the Friday afternoon of the second week, after a meeting between the three of them, Case asked her to, 'Stay a moment, will you?' as she and the builder were preparing to leave.

She paused. 'Sure,' she said, her legs suddenly feeling like treacle beneath her. Almost two weeks had passed and this was the first time he'd asked her to stay behind. So far their arrangements had been conducted on a purely business footing, with Case making no attempt to see her out of working hours. Not that her carefully arranged schedule had given him much chance.

'I know you're a busy lady, but you have to eat,' Case said as the builder left them alone, the three having planned to meet again the next morning—a Saturday meeting for the first time, at Case's insistence. 'How about having dinner with me?'

She swallowed. She'd managed to arrange their previous meetings for earlier in the day than this.

114

Today, though, in order to fit in with Case's work schedule, she'd agreed to a later than usual meeting, driving straight into town after finishing work at five. It was now going on for six-thirty.

She glanced down at her pleated skirt and plain soft wool sweater. 'I'm not dressed for dinner,' she pointed out. Not for the sort of places you go to, she thought.

'We don't have to go anywhere dressy. Like Chinese?'

'Sure, if you do.' How cool and calm she sounded! Inside, she felt anything *but* cool and calm, panic rioting through her. He's just offering you a bite of dinner, not planning to race you off to seduce you, she chided herself, the very notion causing her stomach to churn even more.

'We can walk there,' Case said as they took the lift down to the ground floor. 'The place I have in mind is just off Little Bourke Street. In China Town.'

China Town. She'd eaten at a few restaurants there on her rare trips to town. Casual, inexpensive places. The restaurant Case chose, however, was the last place she would have expected. She almost balked when he led her into the famous Flower Drum, the most exclusive Chinese restaurant in town.

'This is your idea of a modest little Chinese place?' she hissed at him. 'Look at those people ahead of us. . . they're dressed up to the nines.'

'So? People can dress up or come casual. . .anything goes.' His gaze swept over her. 'I don't know what you're worried about. . .you look great to me. You'd look great in a sack.'

'Thanks,' she said drily. Backhanded compliment or not, her spirits lifted a little.

There *was* a wide range of dress, she noted with relief. . .from smart casual, to businesslike, to extreme chic. But she still wished she was wearing something a bit smarter than a pleated checked skirt and perfectly plain beige jumper. She felt even more dowdy when a woman at a nearby table, sitting with a sleek-haired man in a dark business suit, caught Case's eye and waved, flashing a bright red-lipped smile and a wrist jangling with gold bracelets. She was a real glamour puss, her figure-hugging black mini dress showing her voluptuous figure to full advantage.

Lucy sighed, wishing she'd had the sense to foresee Case's dinner invitation. All she'd done before leaving work was brush her hair and put some fresh lipstick on.

Case gave the woman a brief half-smile, raising a hand in a desultory wave, showing no inclination to go over and speak to her.

An old flame? Lucy wondered. She'd be his type, if the rumours about his womanising were true. Glamorous, coolly sophisticated, with expensive tastes. She gritted her teeth, feeling even more out of place now. At least no one could possibly mistake *her* for one of his women! They'd assume she must be his country cousin, or his accountant or something.

She suppressed a giggle. She wasn't normally so self-deprecating. But then, she wasn't normally in the company of one of the country's most eligible, most successful men, and she didn't normally waltz into up-market restaurants dressed like a—like a frumpy suburban working girl!

Case turned back to her with a wry smile. 'Let's hope she doesn't decide to descend on us.'

'She's not a close friend, then?' Lucy asked sweetly.

'I took her out a couple of times,' Case admitted matter-of-factly. 'Daphne's the type of woman you can easily take up and just as easily put down. . .if you know what I mean.' The cynicism, the world-weariness was back in his voice, laced with a hint of mordant humour. Lucy was surprised at his frankness. He didn't strike her as the type who'd trust too many people with his confidences.

He was probably just trying to give her morale a boost, with all this competition around.

'Oh, Daphne's entertaining enough—even amusing in her own over-the-top way,' Case conceded. 'But it's all surface dazzle. Nothing much underneath. She's probably spent all afternoon at a beauty salon,' he added with a derisive lift of his lip. 'You'd never need to do that.' His dark gaze captured her. 'You come straight from work, and you look a million dollars. You don't need trappings or artifice. You have a natural glow from inside.'

She blinked. Outrageously unlikely as the compliment was, she should just accept it. Accept it gracefully and shut up. But something inside her rebelled against what was undoubtedly just a line...a line he'd used a thousand times before.

'That's very big-hearted of you,' she said in a bantering tone, wishing at the same time that she could pluck her gaze away from his, 'but my ego doesn't need bolstering, thank you, Mr Travers. I'm not looking to compete with anyone,' she asserted airily. Let alone with a woman like that, she thought. Even if I could.

'I should hope not,' Case drawled. 'Anyway, you'd have no need to.'

It *was* just a line. It must be. Finding it difficult to escape the darkly compelling gaze, she resorted to attack, asking curiously, 'Is that all women are to you, Case? Entertaining objects to pick up easily and just as easily put down?'

Case was the one who broke eye contact first, glancing up as a waiter brought their pre-dinner drinks. And then he surprised her by answering her question. 'That's all they have been...all I've wanted them to be...since my marriage broke up. Yes.' He spoke tonelessly, cynicism etched deep in his cheeks.

'Your wife must have hurt you very much,' Lucy said in a low voice, wondering what kind of woman she must have been to let a man like Case out of her clutches.

She must have known him, presumably, before he

became the jaded, disillusioned cynic he was today, the ruthless big-shot who picked up and discarded women at will, only wanting them for their entertainment value—and for their bodies too, no doubt. His ex-wife was, in all likelihood, the one who had *made* him that way. Divorced people, she thought broodingly, carried a lot of baggage. Painful baggage. Look at her mother. Look at her brother.

Case caught her gaze again, his dark eyes more thoughtful, it struck her, than pained.

'I think,' he answered slowly, 'it was knowing I'd failed in my marriage that hurt me more. I didn't go into it expecting it to fail.'

She took a quick breath. What was he saying? That losing his wife hadn't caused him pain? That he no longer had any feelings for her? Even if he had, she sensed instinctively, he'd be too proud a man to admit it. Either way, he'd obviously taken his marriage vows seriously. And having failed—and being a man not used to failure—he'd been dead set against marriage ever since, determined not to risk a repeat of his one big mistake.

Whereas she... She sighed under cover of the huge menu a hovering waiter had handed to her. Despite her break-up with David, despite her parents' divorce and her brother Mike's divorce, she still believed in marriage. . .*with the right man*.

And it would be just her luck, dammit, if the right man, the one man in the world she wanted, turned out to be Case Travers—a man totally out of her reach, out of her league! If she didn't take care, Case could very well do to her what *she* had done to David. Let her get close, keep her dangling on a string with no intention of making a commitment, then finally ditch her!

Was she crazy, agreeing to come out to dinner with him, knowing how vulnerable she was to him, and how many worlds apart they were? Was she crazy to want to go on seeing him at all? To go on working for him?

Crazy or not, she knew she *would* keep on working for him. Never to see him again... She didn't even want to think about it!

'Spoken to your mother since you've been back?' Case asked, after they'd placed their order from a range of delicacies she'd never even seen on a Chinese menu before!

'My mother? Yes, a couple of times.' She avoided his eyes as she reached for her glass of mineral water. She'd ordered a safe pre-dinner drink, knowing there'd be wine with dinner.

'She enjoyed her weekend away?'

Lucy raised her glass and took a deep sip. Was he really interested? Or was he just asking about her mother to avoid talking about himself and his ex-wife?

'She said she did.' Her mother hadn't actually said much about her bus trip with Avril. She'd been too busy firing questions at *her*. Having heard about the air strike, she'd given her the third degree until in the end she'd managed to worm it out of her...that Case Travers had stayed on at Surfers too. After which Lucy had had to suffer a fresh spate of maternal warnings about wealthy men in powerful positions preying on vulnerable young girls for their 'fleeting gratification'.

How on earth would Charlotte react when she heard her daughter was now *working* for Case Travers? So far Lucy had managed to avoid mentioning it, cutting short her phone calls to her mother with excuses about being busy and having to rush off.

'Your mother knows you're not seeing David any more?'

She glanced up and nodded, her mouth twisting a little. Her mother had been pleased to hear it, believing she'd done the right thing. But Charlotte would be bound to have second thoughts when she found out that her daughter was now working for *Case Travers* in her spare time. Leaping straight from the frying pan, her mother would call it, into the proverbial fire!

'I hope she wasn't too upset,' Case said, watching her in a way that made her look away quickly.

'My mother only wants what's best for me,' she said primly.

She wasn't going to tell Case that her mother was *happy* that she'd broken up with David. He might get the idea that Charlotte had richer pickings in mind for her daughter. And whatever her mother might be, she wasn't *that* kind of mother. To Charlotte, the kind of person you were and how you felt about someone was more important than money or fame or possessions.

It was strange, Lucy mused, that her mother advocated love so strongly when it was obvious she'd never had a flaming passion for her own husband, the husband she'd finally divorced, or he for her. But then, maybe that was the reason Charlotte wanted something better, more enduring for her daughter.

'Have you made any plans yet to see your mother?' Case's voice broke into her thoughts. 'She must be upset that she missed seeing you when you were up there last month.'

Lucy shrugged. 'She'd like me to fly up for her birthday on Saturday week. . .but I haven't made any definite plans as yet.'

'Then you should.' He paused, then asked, 'You've mentioned to her that you're doing this consultancy work for me?'

Lucy toyed with her glass, avoiding his eye. 'I haven't really had a chance yet,' she said carelessly, and deliberately steered the subject away from her mother to comment on a hot news item she'd read in the paper at lunchtime.

When they returned later in the evening to the head office car park, Case suggested, 'Look, why don't you leave your car here overnight and let me drive you home? I'll pick you up in the morning and we can drive

into town together for our meeting with the builder.
You can pick up your car then.'

She took a quick breath. 'Thanks, but I'll be fine.
Anyway, it would be out of your way.'

'No, it isn't. You live in Surrey Hills, don't you?'

'Ye-es. But I thought you lived here in town.' David
had told her once that Case lived here in the head
office building. . .in the penthouse suite.

'I use my flat here if I want to stay in town overnight.
But mostly I go home to Canterbury. I've moved back
into my parents' old home,' he explained.

Lucy felt a coil of warmth snake through her.
Canterbury was only a suburb away from Surrey
Hills. . .light years away though his house and his street
would be compared to hers. She wondered if living in
his old home was hard for him with all the memories
of his parents that must linger there.

'You live on your own?' she asked, and at once
wished she could catch back the question. It might give
him the idea that she wanted him to take her back
there. The very thought made her insides flutter like
trapped butterflies.

He answered in a lazy drawl, 'I have a retired couple
who live in. Jean cooks and takes care of the house and
Bill looks after the garden and any maintenance. Which
works well, as I travel a fair bit.'

She let her breath out slowly as he waved her to his
car without waiting for her consent. If there were other
people living in his house it was unlikely he'd be
planning to lure her back there tonight. If and when
Case Travers had seduction in mind, he'd use the
privacy of his city penthouse.

Her cheeks burned as her mind conjured up a
procession of glamorous women sharing his bathroom. . .sharing his bed. How many broken hearts had
he left in his wake? Assuming the cool sophisticates he
chose to dally with had hearts to break. Her hand
unconsciously fluttered to the region of her own heart.

At least Gaby would be at home if he happened to
have *her* place in mind for a little dalliance. She felt
breathless at the thought and gulped in a mouthful of
air. He's only offering you a lift home, for heaven's
sake! she told herself, and gave herself a mental shake.
For her own self-preservation she had to keep her head
and guard her heart where Case Travers was concerned. One thing she knew: *he* would never be the
one who'd end up with a broken heart!

When Case pulled up outside her rented house in
Surrey Hills—a small timber place with a pocket-sized
garden—she thanked him and fumbled for the
doorhandle.

'You're not going to invite me in for coffee?'

She paused, her heart skittering. 'If. . .you'd like to.
You could meet my flatmate Gaby.' She was letting
him know they wouldn't be alone and hoping in the
same breath that Gaby wouldn't already have gone to
bed!

'Mmm. . .maybe best not to descend on Gaby at this
hour, without warning,' Case murmured. He touched
her arm. 'I was hoping we might be alone for a few
minutes.'

'Alone? What for?' Her eyes leapt to his. His touch
was like an electric shock, sending tiny explosive cur-
rents crackling through her.

'What for? Here. . . I'll demonstrate.' He leaned
towards her, the leather seat creaking under his weight
as he closed the small gap between them.

She caught her breath as his hand slid over her bare
throat, his fingers surprisingly warm on her skin, her
nerve-ends ultra-sensitive to his touch. He curled his
fingers round her nape, sliding them through her soft
hair, applying gentle pressure to draw her face closer
to his. As his mouth touched hers she made no protest,
letting her lips soften and part under his, finding the
taste and the moist warmth of his lips irresistibly

enticing. If all he wanted was a goodnight kiss. . .well, why not? She could handle that!

But as his kiss deepened and she felt her limbs weakening, turning to liquid fire, as she felt the urge to melt against him and respond in the way his sensual lips, his roaming hands and her own body were urging her to, danger bells started jangling, and she tugged her mouth away with a gasped, 'I'd better go!'

He released her with a promptness that startled her. 'Yes. . .maybe you'd better.' There was irony mingled with a faint huskiness in his voice. And something else she couldn't read. Did he think she was playing a clever little game of hard to get? Was that what he was used to from the women in his life? Teasing, feminine games as a playful way of titillating him?

If he only knew that all she was trying to do was avoid getting hopelessly, helplessly entangled—emotionally—and ending up heartbroken when he waltzed off with the next good-looking female who tweaked his jaded interest. She almost wished he was showing some sign of irritation, or anger, even. It would make it so much easier for her to walk away.

As she clawed at the doorhandle she felt his arm reach across to help her, heard him growl close to her ear, his lips brushing her fevered skin, 'I've wanted to do that ever since our night at Surfers.'

She went still, flicking her tongue over lips turned suddenly dry. Did he mean the night he'd fleetingly kissed her at the door?

She swung her head away, steeling herself to mock lightly, 'I'll just bet you have. . .if what I've heard about you is true! You have quite a reputation for kissing women, Case Travers. *Lots* of women.' For a startling second she felt a stab of what could only be jealousy at the thought of those warmly sensual lips on someone else's.

'Oh? You've been following my amorous adventures, have you?' He sounded more amused than chastened!

She felt her cheeks burning in the darkness. 'I see you're not denying you have them.' She managed a taunting smile. 'Just as long as you're not expecting me to join the queue.' Might as well let him know right now that she had no intention of being one of his here-today-gone-tomorrow bedmates, dewy-eyed suburban push-over though he might think her.

'Who said anything about a queue?' His tone was pained. 'I haven't looked at another woman since the day I first met you. Doesn't that tell you something?'

Her heart jumped. Was that true? If it was, it told her something, all right. It told her that his invitation to come and work for him must have been the clever first step of a calculated campaign. He was looking for a new amorous adventure, and for some reason he'd singled her out as a prime candidate. Heaven knew why. She must be as far removed from his usual glamorous, ultra-sophisticated conquests as Venus was from Earth!

Perhaps that was it. A jaded high-flyer, blessed with everything a man could possibly want, looking for something different, for fresh new fields to conquer. Amusing himself, for a change, by chasing after a woman who wasn't all surface dazzle and worldly sophistication. The attraction of a seasoned rake for a fresh-faced innocent?

I'll show you I'm no fresh-faced innocent, she thought spiritedly.

'It tells me you've been too busy and hard-working since you've been back to make time for your usual glittering conquests,' she retorted crisply, trying to ignore the arm still draped across her and the hand that had somehow become entangled with her own on the doorhandle.

Hadn't looked at another woman, indeed! He hadn't exactly been pounding on her door since she'd been back. Tonight was the first time they'd been out together socially, other than that lunch he'd inveigled her into the day he'd asked her to work for him. Since then they'd met often enough, but only at their daytime gym meetings, with the builder present on each occasion. Outside working hours Case had been avoiding her as avidly as she'd been avoiding him! Had he been hoping to drive her wild with frustration and longing? Hah!

When he spoke again, his face was so close to hers that she could almost taste the spicy warmth of his breath.

'Maybe I didn't want to frighten you away.'

Goosebumps shivered over her skin. She felt herself trembling, and drew in a shaky breath, not sure if he was mocking her or if he actually meant it. Case Travers was an experienced, smooth-talking, devilishly clever man. She'd had little experience by comparison.

Just enough to be suspicious.

'And maybe,' his soft voice continued, 'I wanted to be sure you were free of David. Wanted *you* to be sure. Or. . .' He paused, his lips pursing provocatively. 'Maybe I felt that the kid glove approach was the wisest course where you're concerned. .having earned your ire in the past for charging in uninvited and taking over your life.'

Her eyes leapt to his face. But it was impossible to read his expression in the darkness, or judge if he was serious or poking gentle fun at her. The bantering note in his voice suggested the latter. She'd be crazy to trust him for a minute!

'I must go in,' she said, feeling hopelessly out of her depth and hating the feeling. It made her feel far too vulnerable—a new feeling for her.

'I didn't mean to scare you away.' Pressing his thumb down on the doorhandle, he gave the door a gentle push, before finally withdrawing his arm.

She heard the smile in his voice, and wondered again if he was playing some clever little game of his own. . . a silken game of subtle seduction, gently leading her to where he wanted her to be. Under his spell. In his power. And ultimately. . .in his bed!

'Before you go. . .' His voice curled round her as she swung her legs out of the car. 'How about coming to the footy with me tomorrow, after our gym meeting in the morning? The Demons are playing Collingwood at the MCG. Should be a great match.'

She paused, her heart missing a beat. 'I'm already going. With my brother.' She lifted her chin, her eyes flashing a challenge. 'You're welcome to join us if you like. If you're prepared to sit in the stands with the plebs.' Now she was the one who was taunting *him*, knowing full well that Maxi Board owned a private box at the MCG and that Case Travers could watch the game in comfort from behind a shield of glass, well removed from the common crowd below.

His lip curled into that charismatic half-smile she found so hard to resist. 'I'll have you know I often sit in the stands—and quite happily too,' he told her blithely, 'on the weekends when my team plays away from home. When I'm at the MCG, however, I don't *need* to sit in the stands. And tomorrow you won't need to either, Lucy. I'm inviting you and your brother to spend the day in Maxi Board's box. . .as my guests.'

Stifling her surprise, and a flare of something else that she repressed quickly, she said guardedly, 'That's kind of you, Case, but I'm not sure we'd want to be sealed up in a closed box all day, away from the crowd. . .away from the atmosphere. Besides,' she warned him, 'my brother, gentle as he normally is, can be a very noisy barracker. I'm sure you wouldn't want—'

'You should hear some of our guests,' Case broke in drily. 'I've been known to get a bit vocal myself. You'll get a free lunch,' he coaxed. 'And afternoon tea.'

'Oh, well, that makes all the difference,' she retorted. Who else would be going? she wondered dubiously. The cream of Melbourne society? Or stuffy business-

types, more interested in their wheeling and dealing
than in the footy, with flashy wives or girlfriends in
tow, keen to socialise and gossip rather than watch the
game? If she went, she'd have to be sociable too. And
dress to suit. She could hardly wear her normal footy
gear—jeans and a parka, with a red and blue scarf
draped round her neck.

'Is that a yes?'

How unbelievably smug he looked! 'I'm. . .not sure,'
she prevaricated, determined not to jump at the invitation. 'You don't even know my brother. And
anyway. . .you must feel isolated and out of things,
sitting up there in a glass box, so far away from the
action!'

'Not really. You get a great view over the whole
ground. And we try to choose guests with some interest
in the game. Overseas visitors lap it up. My brother-in-
law, John Castle, will be there tomorrow too, as joint
host. You've met him, I understand?'

She nodded, wondering how he knew. Had they been
discussing her? 'Once. . .yes.'

She'd met John at a house-warming barbecue he and
his wife had thrown at their new home in Kew a few
months ago for the senior staff at Maxi Board. David
had taken her along with him. Case would have been
there too, David had mentioned, only he'd been overseas at the time. She remembered John and his heavily
pregnant wife Mardi as genial hosts who'd made her
feel welcome at their lovely new home. She wondered
if they knew she'd since split up with David. Would
that make things awkward?

Seeing her still wavering, Case added swiftly, 'And
I'd like to meet your brother.' His smile stretched, his
eyes darkly persuasive. 'You might be surprised. You
might even enjoy it.'

She smiled back, doubting it. But she was prepared
to try anything once. Besides, a free lunch wasn't to be

sneezed at. Even if she would have to be on her best behaviour.

'I'll ask Mike and see what he says,' she agreed finally. 'Can I let you know first thing in the morning?'

'Sure. But try to persuade him. I reckon it's going to be a close match tomorrow. If he intends to drive into town, he can park in our head office building. We'll go together in my car; I have a parking spot at the ground.'

Of course he did. Naturally.

'Would Mike need to wear a suit?' she asked.

'Hell, no. Nor a tie. Only blokes coming straight from work wear suits. A sports jacket, sweater—whatever's comfortable.'

'I'll tell him.'

Mike, she thought, would probably be the one persuading *her* to go. He liked meeting people, especially since his divorce, and in his amiable way he got on with most people. Apart from his ex-wife. But she'd been so neurotic, even a saint would have failed to make her happy. She'd put poor Mike through the wringer before he'd finally given up and walked out. He was still reeling, still wary of women. A bit like Case Travers, she thought with a sigh. Wary of committing himself a second time.

'Goodnight, Case,' she said, hauling herself out of the car at last. 'Thank you for the dinner. It was lovely.' This time he didn't try to stop her as she swung on her heel and hastily made her escape.

CHAPTER EIGHT

CASE ushered her into the air-conditioned warmth of Maxi Board's private box ahead of Mike and himself. A few people were already there, standing around chatting and sipping drinks. Two tables were set up for lunch nearby. The women looked no more flashy, Lucy noted with relief, than she did in her tailored trousers and loose matching jacket. And at least they looked friendly enough as they glanced round with ready smiles. She began to relax.

Looking beyond them, she could see rows of seats leading down to huge plate glass windows overlooking the ground. She had to admit there was a superb view over the entire ground from up here. Surprisingly, it didn't feel anywhere near as remote as she'd been expecting—though Mike's binoculars would certainly come in handy.

One of the men, reddish-haired and about Case's age, in his mid-thirties, broke away from the group. 'Well, if it isn't Lucy Farrell. How are you?'

Lucy smiled, recognising David's ex-boss, John Castle—Maxi Board's general manager, Case's brother-in-law. She was surprised that he'd remembered her name when they'd only met that once, with other people there.

'I was so happy to hear about your baby son, Mr Castle,' she said formally. 'How is he? And your wife?'

'Oh, call me John, please. Young James is just fine. Mardi too. She won't be coming today, though. She wanted to stay at home with the baby.'

Lucy saw him flick a curious glance in Mike's direction. Was he wondering if she'd found a new boyfriend, now that David had moved interstate? As David's ex-boss, John must be aware that they'd parted company before David's transfer to Sydney.

'I'd like you to meet my brother, Mike Farrell,' she said, before Case could do the honours.

As the two shook hands Case put in silkily, 'Lucy is my consultant, John, on the new head office gym. Which means we've been seeing quite a bit of each other.'

Was he implying that it had already become more than a mere working relationship? Lucy tried hard not to flush, not to show any reaction. His kiss last night—and his invitation here today—seemed to suggest that Case *wanted* more. And since she'd allowed him to kiss her, he must think that she wanted more too. He would reason, no doubt, that they were both single adults who enjoyed each other's company, so why not have a bit of harmless fun while they were working together?

And it sounded as if he didn't care who knew it!

Just as he wouldn't care, wouldn't give her another thought, when it was over?

She tightened her lips as Case stood back to let a hovering waitress take their drink orders. No, of course he wouldn't care! And he would expect her to have the same free and easy attitude, to be adult about it and play by the rules, as the other women he'd dallied with since his marriage break-up had been expected to do. Easy come, easy go. . .

She stole a furtive glance at Case as he turned aside to welcome a new young couple into the box, his face crinkling into that lopsided, achingly attractive smile that even now made her knees go to water just at the sight of it. Oh, Case, she thought with a sigh. If only I *could* play the easy come, easy go game you seem to want! But I don't think I can. . .not with you. I'd never survive. . .not in one piece. Not the way I feel about you already.

* * *

'Well, Lucy. . . Was it so bad being stuck in a corporate box?' Case asked as the three of them headed for the car park after the match. His dark eyes were still gleaming with elation after the Demons' thrilling three-point victory in one of the most exciting matches of the season so far.

'It was great,' she conceded, feeling equally ecstatic over the win, and surprised at how much she *had* enjoyed the experience of watching the match from an exclusive private box, far above the crowd she normally sat with.

It had been a fun day. For Mike too. There had been lively rivalry between the followers of both teams, and equally lively barracking. And later in the afternoon, when the winter sun had finally burst through the clouds, they'd thrown open the windows overlooking the ground, letting in the roar of the crowd as well as a burst of fresh air.

'How would you like to meet my new nephew?' Case asked as he drove them back to his car park in town. 'John and Mardi are popping over to my place in an hour to celebrate the Demons' win over a pizza and a glass of bubbly. Why don't you both join us?'

Mike glanced at Lucy to gauge her reaction. She drew in her breath, not sure what her reaction *was*. Case puzzled her. For a man supposedly set on seduc-tion, a man who liked engaging in meaningless, short-lived relationships, he wasn't exactly rushing to be alone with her. . .let alone rushing her into his bed. Was he hoping to lull her into a false sense of security by having his family join them? Hoping to get her alone later?

She drew in a quivery breath.

One thing she knew: Case was hardly indulging in a leisurely, old-fashioned courting ritual, with a wedding ring as the ultimate prize! He'd made it plain he'd lost faith in love and marriage. If she kept that in mind, she'd be better able to guard her far too susceptible heart. Best to keep in mind, too, that as a divorced man, cynical about marriage, he'd be a bad risk anyway.

'Well... OK,' she agreed, knowing she would have her car if she needed a quick escape route. 'I'd love to meet your new nephew. Mike, you'll come too, won't you?' She'd already offered Mike a lift from town, knowing he'd left his car at home and caught a tram in.

Mike answered the appeal he saw in her eye. 'Fine with me.' He raised his brow a fraction, and she swallowed and imperceptibly shook her head.

Back at Maxi Board's car park, Case gave them his address and drove off first, with Lucy following in her own car with Mike. She wasn't surprised when Mike asked, now that they were alone, 'What's going on with you two?'

'Going on?' she echoed innocently. 'Nothing. I'm just doing some work for him. On his new gym.'

'You like him, don't you? And, if I'm not mistaken, he likes you too.'

She gave a snort to cover an odd little tremor inside. 'Not the way you're thinking,' she said drily. 'He's divorced and never intends to get serious about anyone again, let alone ever marry again. And if he ever did change his mind, can you see him tripping down the aisle with a sports-mad podiatrist from the suburbs? The great Case Travers? And I'm certainly not interested in anything else he might have in mind, so you can forget it, OK?' And she pointedly changed the subject.

The Travers' family home, now Case's home, was in Canterbury's most exclusive street, a magnificent old house set in a vast, immaculately kept garden. Seeing it, Lucy felt the gap between her and Case widen to a gaping chasm. This was his world...this grandeur, this breathtaking wealth, this comfortable affluence. He'd been born to it, born to live in a street where business leaders and famous politicians had their homes, born to mix with the rich and powerful.

Not that her own old home and background were anything to be ashamed of. Her parents—her suburban bank manager father and her finance-trained mother, who'd worked part-time in a school office during her children's school years—had made sure that their son and daughter weren't deprived. But they'd never moved in these exclusive, moneyed circles. In fact, they'd had a hefty mortgage on their home for years, and it had been a struggle at times for their parents to keep them both at private schools.

The married couple who normally lived in at Case's home were away for the weekend, she discovered with a renewed flutter of nerves. Had Case sent them away deliberately? But then she remembered that she had her own car, and that she had Mike to drop home afterwards, so anything Case might have in mind for later in the evening was purely in her own mind. Or futile wishful thinking in his!

Contrarily, she was aware of a slight twinge, almost of disappointment!

Inside, Case's home was elegant, spacious and comfortable, rather than opulent and grandly intimidating. Warm, soft furnishings lent an intimate air to the long-windowed, high-ceilinged rooms. It was a surprisingly livable family home. She wondered if Case found it difficult living here, in a family home made for a married couple...children...fun and laughter. But then, it was his old childhood home, so presumably he had warm memories to sustain him, lonely as it must be for him here at times. And his work, running the giant Travers group of companies, must occupy a fair chunk of his time. He regularly travelled interstate, from all reports, and often overseas.

And what a cosy place to bring his women! What a way to keep any loneliness at bay! He merely had to send his live-in couple away for the weekend or overnight, and *voilà*! A perfect love-nest!

Why should the lurid images that immediately sprang

to mind—images of other women in his house, in his arms, in his *bed*—cause a swift pang inside her? Disgusted, she blinked the disturbing images away.

Case led them both into a comfortably inviting family room at the rear of the house—a huge room lined with bookshelves, stereo equipment and a TV set. Deep armchairs and sofas were scattered about, and a cosy gas fire glowed warmly. The room overlooked a broad expanse of lawn, with a pool and a shower block on one side and a grass tennis court beyond that. This place had everything!

'Make yourselves comfortable while I pour you a drink and order the pizzas,' Case invited, waving a hand towards a soft leather sofa. 'John and Mardi should be— Ah!' He broke off as the front doorbell shrilled. 'Here they are now!'

It was a surprisingly enjoyable evening. They all cooed over the new baby, a bright-eyed little boy with his father's red hair and an engaging smile, while Mardi, the proud mother, was as warm and friendly as Lucy remembered from their once-only previous meeting.

Case, she thought pensively, watching as he played with his small nephew, was obviously a family-orientated man under that cynical, cold-hearted façade. What a pity his marriage had soured him and made him so set against ever trying marriage again. He had so much to offer the right woman.

The right woman. . . She gulped, her eyes dilating as she watched him. *I* could be the right woman for you, Case Travers, she thought. If only our worlds weren't a million miles apart. And you could be the right man for me. . .if you could forget our different backgrounds and learn to believe in love and marriage again.

Her body began to tremble at the startling thought, her lips parting involuntarily as she stared at Case.

It was at that precise moment that Case turned his head and caught her eye.

His face froze under her gaze. He seemed abruptly to turn to stone. Oh, dear God, she thought in panic, he's seen it. He's seen how I feel about him and it's the last thing he wants, a complication like that in his life!

With a supreme effort, she forced a bright, careless smile to her lips and tugged her gaze away from his, hoping he would decide he'd been mistaken. Trying to convince herself that *she* was mistaken, that what she felt for him was just a physical attraction for a sexy, charismatic man, nothing more.

Her hands shook as she picked at the Hawaiian pizza on her plate and sipped the champagne in her glass, with a breathless ache in her throat and emotions swirling through her. She had to pull herself together, face reality, stifle such futile feelings. And the sooner the better.

Was Case treating her a trifle guardedly now, after that look, or was she, in her heightened emotional state, imagining it? It was hard to tell. He was courteous and attentive enough. But he seemed to be avoiding meeting her eye, and if inadvertently he did so, it was only for a fleeting instant, before his gaze flicked away.

You won't see him again for dust after tonight, she silently berated herself. Men like Case Travers run for cover if they think a woman's getting emotionally attached to them. Case might have been planning—hoping—to have an amusing little romp with you, but that was all he'd have wanted—he'd steer clear of anything that threatened to become heavy. Messy.

Damn, she thought, feeling like kicking herself. Damn! Now she'd spoiled everything!

But when she and Mike bade Case goodnight at her car later in the evening, Case turned to her with an easy smile and said, in front of Mike, 'You're welcome to use my pool any time you like, Lucy, for your morning dip. It's heated, and a darned sight more pleasant, I'd imagine, than a public pool. When I'm

home I always go for a dip before breakfast. Feel free
to join me. Why don't you come Monday morning?
Mike, you're welcome to come too, if you're into early-
morning dips at this time of year.'

Before Lucy could open her mouth, Mike answered
with a grin, 'I leave any early-morning exercise to my
sister...thanks all the same, Case. But you take up the
offer, Lu. It would be closer for you to come here, and
you wouldn't have to worry about other swimmers
getting in your way.'

If Case's eyes hadn't been on her, she would have
glared at Mike, or nudged him into shutting up. As it
was, she stood wavering, torn between turning her back
on Case and accepting his offer. She didn't want to lose
Case Travers from her life, that was the bottom line.
And if he was inviting her, for whatever reason, to stay
in touch... She took a deep breath, finally forcing her
tongue to unlock.

'That's kind of you,' she said, adding lightly, 'Thanks.
Monday, then. Is six-thirty too early?'

'Perfect,' Case said, and though he was smiling the
glance he gave her was cursory, his dark eyes shadowed
in the diffused glow of the driveway lamps.

A moment later she was in her car driving off...
surreptitiously watching Case in the rear vision mirror
as she steered the car along the sweeping curve of the
driveway to the front gates. He was standing where
she'd left him, his eyes on her car, his powerful body
immobile, like a rock. He seemed deep in thought, his
hands thrust deep into his pockets.

She would have given the world to know what he
was thinking. Why, for heaven's sake, if he wanted to
avoid getting any more involved with her, was he
inviting her back to his home, wanting to see more of
her?

And why had she agreed?

* * *

When Case greeted her in the misty dawn of Monday morning for their pre-breakfast swim, his smile seemed genuinely welcoming, his dark eyes warm and friendly as they met hers.

'I wasn't sure you'd turn up,' he confessed, running his gaze over her practical tracksuit and runners and the carry-all she'd slung over her shoulder. 'It's pretty cold these mornings. Come on through.'

He, she noticed, her skin prickling at the sight of him, was wearing a towelling bathrobe that exposed his firm strong legs from his bare knees down to the loose scuffs on his feet. His hair was still rumpled from his night's sleep, his strong jaw shadowed with overnight growth. The intimacy of the scene struck her dumb for a second, and she was relieved when he led her into the kitchen and introduced her to his housekeeper Jean, who was already up and dressed and getting breakfast under way.

A trim, fading blonde of uncertain age, Jean showed no reaction at the sight of a pretty young woman in her boss's house at dawn other than a polite diffidence. Case had obviously prepared her. Maybe she was *used* to her boss inviting women to his home at any hour of the day or night.

Hold onto that thought, Lucy Farrell, she told herself.

Despite the chilly air round the pool, it was wonderful in the water, the temperature just right. It was a luxurious feeling having a pool all to themselves. . .far more pleasant than the noisy, steamy indoor pool she normally used. Or was it having Case there with her that made it so pleasurable?

As she was doing her usual steady laps of the pool Case lapped them with her, surprising her by keeping up with her. David had never been able to. Had never even tried.

As she paused for a breather, floating on her back, Case bobbed up near where her toes were poking out

of the water. Before she'd worked out what he had in
mind, he'd caught her left foot in his hand, lowered his
head and was sucking her toes, one by sensuous one!

She gave a slightly breathless laugh. She'd never felt
anything quite so erotic, so deliciously, shiveringly
pleasurable. She'd been treating feet all her working
life, without realising they promised such voluptuous,
sensual delights!

She stifled a faint moan when he finally lifted his
head, freeing her foot. 'A hard-working podiatrist
needs a bit of foot-care herself on occasion,' he murmured, a mocking light in his eyes even as something
in the dark depths smouldered under the surface glitter.
She found herself mesmerised by the drops of water
glistening on the ends of his lashes. 'Ready for breakfast?' he asked. 'I'm starving.'

The thought of breakfast brought her back to earth.
That, and the suspicion that he was attempting to break
the spell he'd cast over her, make light of his
impromptu toe-sucking exercise.

'Sure.' Her voice was a trifle husky, and she mentally
grimaced as she heard it. 'Ready when you are.'

They hauled themselves out of the pool, shaking
water from their hair as they reached for their towels,
both still breathing heavily from their exertions. Or
was it from something else?

She tried not to think about it.

'That was great!' she gasped. 'Invigorating!' Let him
think she was breathless from her swim, not from him!'

'You'd better hop into the shower before your teeth
start rattling,' Case advised. They'd left their gear in
the changing rooms by the pool. 'See you in the kitchen
in ten minutes.'

'You don't have to give me breakfast as well,' she
protested. 'I'll grab something when I go home to get
ready for work.'

'Of course you'll have breakfast. Jean will be disappointed if you don't. In fact, tomorrow morning why

don't you bring your work clothes with you and go straight to work from here? You won't have to rush back home to change then.'

Swallowing, she shook her head, trying to ignore the way her heart was thrashing about in her chest at his offer. 'You don't want me hanging around when you're getting ready for work,' she argued, still breathless, her emotions as chaotic as her thoughts. One minute Case seemed to be backing off, the next. . . Why did he blow hot and cold? 'The idea was just to pop in for a swim and then go,' she reminded him unsteadily. 'I'm sure you must want to read the morning papers. . .or listen to the radio. . .or make phone calls or whatever. I'll just—'

'I can do all that when I get to work.' Case was looking amused now, a mocking lift to his brow. 'Jean likes fussing over people, and she doesn't often get the chance. I'm away a fair bit. In fact, I'm off to Sydney later this morning, for three days. I've some negotiating to do with the government up there, as well as meetings to attend. I can't get back any sooner. But you must still come, Lucy, even while I'm away. I've told Jean to expect you.'

She looked up at him. 'Why are you being so kind to me?' she demanded, the question leaping out.

He seemed to tense, as if she'd caught him off guard. 'I'm not being kind.' He smiled, a sardonic curve of his lips. 'I want your company. . .simple as that. I want to see more of you. There! Now are you satisfied?'

She caught her breath at the admission, but at the same time noted the muscle flicking at his jaw, the guarded look in his eye that was impossible to read. . . as if he wasn't saying everything he could be saying, as if something—some problem within himself, could it be?—was holding him back.

Her heart shrivelled. He wanted to see more of her. . .and yet he didn't. He was attracted to her. . .but he was fighting it. He was going on seeing her against

his better judgement. She wasn't suitable. She wasn't
his type. The right type. He was afraid she might cause
trouble if he went too far, make demands on him. He
preferred women he could feel confident would play by
his rules. Easy come, easy go.

'Look, you're shivering,' Case said abruptly, almost
giving her a push. 'Get into that shower!'

As she stood under the stream of hot water she tried
to find a more acceptable reason for the tension, the
wariness in him. She found herself hoping it wasn't
personal after all, but simply a lingering mistrust of
women in general as a result of his failed marriage.
Hoping it was just a fear of commitment, of entrusting
his heart to another woman.

Had the scars from his broken marriage really gone
that deep?

Over breakfast in the bright, cosy nook off the kitchen,
Case was relaxed and solicitous, the tension she'd noted
earlier seeming to have been washed away by his
shower.

'I enjoyed having your brother with us on Saturday,'
he said idly as he reached for a slice of toast. 'To look
at you and Mike together, I would never take you for
brother and sister. He must take after your father.'

'He does. In looks *and* temperament. Even,' Lucy
added with a sigh, 'in having a failed marriage behind
him. . . Though in my father's case it took twenty-odd
years for him to realise he and my mother had made a
mistake. . .or at least to do anything about it.' She
accepted it now, that her parents had never been as
happy as they'd made out, had never been the soul-
mates a husband and wife should be, that they'd both
grown apart long before Beth came on the scene. 'Mike
only needed a year.'

'But Mike didn't have children. . .did he?' Case
pointed out quietly.

'No.' Lucy glanced up at him. 'Would *you* have

stayed with your wife if you'd had children?' she heard herself asking curiously.

Case took a bite of his toast, and swallowed it before replying. 'I can't answer that,' he admitted at length. 'For us to have had children my wife would have needed to be a different person. As it was, she didn't want children...wasn't suited to having them, as I discovered too late... So the situation would never have arisen. It worked out for the best.'

Lucy chewed on her lip. If he thought that, then why was he so wary of close relationships, of venturing into marriage a second time? He must realise that all women weren't like his wife. Or was it a case of once bitten, never again? A successful achiever not wanting to risk failure a second time?

Case switched the conversation back to her family, pondering aloud in a musing tone. 'Maybe your parents were happier than you thought for all those years and they weren't just waiting for you and Mike to grow up and leave home. Maybe it had nothing to do with the woman your father eventually married either. Maybe something happened. Maybe one of them found out something the other had done, say, years earlier, perhaps... I don't know.

'Let's say your father found out something about your mother,' he suggested delicately, 'and it was something that hurt him so much that he turned to someone else for consolation. That might explain why your mother let him go so easily...because she felt that she was in some way to blame...'

'Are you insinuating that my mother had an *affair* while she was married to my father?' Lucy's eyes flashed in quick rejection. 'Why would you think that? Why would you blame my mother for their break-up?' She faced him accusingly. 'Because she's a *woman*?

'You still don't think much of women, do you, Case? You still can't bring yourself to trust a woman...any woman. My mother's a very moral person. She would never have had a hole-and-corner affair! It was my *father* who caused their marriage to break up... because he wanted to marry someone else. It's as simple as that!'

Case held up a placatory hand. 'Sorry... I just thought that maybe it might explain—'

'Well, you're wrong!' Lucy snapped, glaring at him. 'My mother would never have been unfaithful to my father...or he to her, for that matter. Even though Dad was friendly with Beth while he was married— she worked in his bank—he swore to me that they never got together, not in *that* way, until after he'd asked my mother for his freedom...until after they'd separated. Maybe the people in your world play fast and loose in their marriages, but my parents never did!' She could feel her colour rising, along with her indignation.

'Lucy—'

She swept on before he could finish. 'I doubt if my father would even have *left* my mother if she'd been truly cut up about it when he asked her for a divorce. But she took it straight on the chin. She gave him his freedom without a fight or a scene because she knew in her heart that he'd be happier with Beth...sad and hurt as it made her at the time.' She winced at the memory of that painful time. But her mother had survived...without bitterness...or not too much. And she admired Charlotte for her courage, her understanding, her strength of character.

'I see where you get your values, your integrity,' Case said quietly, and he smiled that crooked smile of his and looked suddenly younger, less cynical. He reached across the table to stroke the back of her hand with calming fingers. 'And I do think a lot of women... of one woman in particular...' His black eyes caught hers and burned into the blue depths. 'And I would trust *her* ... with my life.'

She stared back at him, her soft lips parting, hardly able to believe she was hearing the words. But then, almost as if he regretted uttering them, he broke eye contact and drew back his hand to reach for another slice of toast.

'Have you told your mother you've been seeing me?' he asked, without looking up. His face was impassive now, his gaze intent on the toast he was buttering.

'Seeing you?' she echoed, swallowing. Was that what she'd been doing? 'You mean...' She faltered, still shaky from what he'd just said about her—as well as from his touch. 'You mean, does she know that I've been working for you?'

'Well...' His lips quirked. 'If you'd prefer to put it that way.'

She struggled to regain her composure, shrugging airily as she told him, 'I did mention that I was doing some consultancy work for you.' She'd spoken to Charlotte only on Saturday, before leaving for her gym meeting in town, finally letting her mother know what had been keeping her so busy lately. She was anxious to mention it before Mike did. Her brother was likely to make a big thing of it.

'And she wasn't too happy about it, I take it?' Case pursued softly. There was an odd note in his voice now. Not bitterness, not cynicism, barely even irony. He sounded almost...resigned.

She swallowed. 'Why would you think that?' she breathed. And then asked, forcing a bantering note, 'Are you admitting that what people say about your lady-killer reputation is true? But of course, it is true, isn't it?' she ploughed on, hating to ask, but needing to know. 'You told me yourself you like women who are easy to pick up and just as easy to get rid of. Any mother would be wary, hearing that you were anywhere near their daughter!'

Case gave a snort. 'I never said I *liked* women like that. I merely said I'd taken *out* women like that...

knowing they wouldn't expect any more of me than I would of them so long as they had a jewelled memento as a parting gift.' His mouth twisted, the old cynicism back in his voice. 'Forget about them,' he rasped. 'They went away happy and nobody got hurt. To get back to your mother... You mentioned the other day that her birthday's coming up and that she's hoping you'll fly up to Brisbane to share the day with her.'

'That's right.' She nodded, her brow puckering faintly. Why did he keep coming back to her mother? 'It's this coming weekend,' she told him warily. 'Saturday.' As yet she hadn't made any definite plans. She'd told her mother she'd try to fly up...if her work on the gym allowed.

'Well, then...' He pinned her with his gaze. 'How about we both fly up for the weekend and take your mother and her friend Avril out to dinner on Saturday night? We'll have an overnight stay and fly back on Sunday.'

Lucy caught her breath. Why would *Case* want to be involved in her mother's birthday? He didn't even know her. Or Avril either. 'You want to meet my mother?' she asked bluntly. Let him spell out his reasons.

'Is that so strange?' He cocked an eyebrow at her. 'That I should want to meet the mother of the young lady with such delectable toes? You feel I'll be intruding?'

What was he saying? She eyed him with suspicion, stifling the tremor that ran through her. Why did she get the feeling that his answer didn't ring true? They were hardly close. They weren't even casual lovers. Let alone anything more.

She sighed. It didn't make sense. Men like Case Travers—men who steered clear of emotional entanglement—didn't let a woman take him home to meet her mother. Not unless...*Were* his feelings starting to get involved? He'd given no hint of it!

Get real, Lucy, she told herself. Any feelings he had would be purely carnal!

She ran her tongue over her lips. Surely he didn't. . .? Was he seeking her mother's sanction before even starting an *affair* with her? Her mind spun.

'Lucy, stop always looking for reasons or ulterior motives,' Case urged. 'Just go with the flow for once.' His eyes were a dark glitter under the damp tousle of his hair. 'I'm offering to fly you up to Brisbane with me. If your mother doesn't want me involved in her birthday, I'll just drop you off and—'

'Don't be silly.' She gave a brittle laugh. 'I'm sure she won't mind.' Oh, *won't* she? 'I'm just surprised you'd *want* to be involved.'

'Well, there you are. Nice to know I can surprise you at times. You're forever surprising *me*.'

Her hand fluttered to her throat. 'I'll be staying at my mother's,' she blurted out. 'And I'm afraid Avril has only one spare room—a *single* room,' she stressed, in case he had thoughts of sharing it.

Case grinned at her—an amused rather than a rakish grin. 'I have no intention of pushing myself onto Avril and your mother as a house guest. I'll stay at a hotel. I was only suggesting that I join the three of you for your mother's birthday dinner. As your host for the evening—if your mother will allow me.'

He paused, then added smoothly, 'Look. Let's not even mention in advance that I'll be coming with you.' His smile turned wry, deepening the harsh line slashing his left cheek. 'If your mother's so dead set against me, she just might plan another weekend away.'

Lucy bit back a gasp. 'You're not—you can't be implying that my mother went away for that weekend deliberately to avoid *you*?'

He shrugged, taking a sip of his coffee before answering. 'Maybe not. But I'd prefer not to risk it. I'd like to meet her this time, let her make up her own mind about me, face to face, and hopefully win her over.

Deal?' he asked, his eyes again seeking hers, their magnetic force drawing her gaze and holding it captive.

As she stared back at him she felt herself shaking with some powerful, heart-thumping emotion, part thrill, part expectancy, part. . .confusion. 'But why do you care so much?' she whispered. 'Care what my mother thinks of you?' A man as powerful, as successful, as self-assured as Case Travers, caring about the opinion of a mere mother. . .a mere woman. . .a divorced one at that. It took her breath away!

If that was all it was. . .a wish to win her mother over.

She'd love to believe it. But realistically could she honestly see the suave, self-possessed Case Travers tamely seeking a mother's approval before setting out to seduce her daughter? In her dreams! He'd just go ahead and—

'I care more about what *you* think of me,' Case said quietly, and she stopped breathing altogether, the throb of his deep voice rolling all the way through her.

As she sat stunned, wondering if she dared believe him, believe a word he said, he stiffened abruptly, his gaze leaping to his watch.

'I'll have to fly. . . I have a plane to catch.' He was briskly businesslike now, any emotion wiped out. 'I'll be back in town on Thursday. Arrange a meeting with the builder for Thursday afternoon, will you? After work. It'll be our last meeting before work starts on the gym. I'll take you out to dinner afterwards to celebrate a job well done.' The words cracked out, leaving her breathless, with no chance to utter a sound.

'Leave the flight arrangements for the weekend to me,' he went on. 'Just tell your mother you'll be arriving Saturday afternoon and that you'll be taking her out to dinner in the evening. And Avril, of course. Leave my name out of it for the time being.'

He scraped back his chair so forcibly that it wobbled and almost tipped over. Then he strode from the room without looking back, covering the distance in a couple of long strides and leaving Lucy sitting open-mouthed at the table, trembling from head to toe.

CHAPTER NINE

SHE half-heartedly lapped the pool in the frosty early morning, feeling achingly alone for the third morning in a row without Case swimming beside her. She missed him so much, and yet. . .niggling doubts still plagued her. *Why* did he want to meet her mother so much? Was it—could it be possible that he wanted to check out her background, her *suitability*, before getting in any deeper? Before even committing himself to an *affair*?

She felt a stab of hurt anger at the thought. She'd never thought of Case as being class-conscious. . .a snob. Despite his privileged upbringing, his immense wealth and power, he'd always treated her as an equal—or appeared to—disregarding the differences between them.

She rose dripping from the pool, burying her head in her towel with a sigh. Maybe she was trying to read too much into a simple kindness. She must remember Case was a man who made snap decisions, a man used to taking control. She'd mentioned it was her mother's birthday at the weekend and he'd decided on the spur of the moment to join her for the occasion. It could be as simple as that. A rich man's whim.

But deep down she didn't really believe it.

When she saw him again at five o'clock that afternoon for their meeting with the builder, the look in Case's eyes when they first met hers gave her a piercing jolt. For a brief second she glimpsed naked emotion in the black depths, an almost savage yearning, before he snapped his gaze away and got down to business.

When their eyes met again in the course of their

meeting the dark depths of his were hooded, his face set, intent on the job at hand.

After the builder had left them, Case drew an envelope from his pocket and handed it to her. 'This is for all the time and hard work you've spent on this project, Lucy.' His eyes were warm and appreciative now. . .but no more than that. 'Thank you. I appreciate it. Your work's done, but I hope you'll still pop in from time to time to see how the gym is progressing. And if you have any criticisms, or want any modifications made, I'd welcome your suggestions. I still consider you our consultant.'

'Thank you,' Lucy said stiltedly, taking the envelope from him. Her throat had turned dry and her fingers shook as they inadvertently brushed his. The way he spoke. . . Was he leaving it up to her whether she stayed involved in the project or not? Giving her permission to bow out if she wished? Hoping that she would so that he could bow out of *her* life, now that she'd served her purpose? Would he be bowing out of their Brisbane trip next?

She steeled herself to expect it, mentally kicking herself for imagining he'd ever had a personal interest in her, let alone any real feeling for her.

On their way down in the lift she asked carelessly, 'How was Sydney?' She was thinking of David now, wondering how he was getting on. She hadn't heard a word from him since he'd left Melbourne.

'The negotiations went well. My other meetings too. Our Sydney operations are in good shape. David seems to be thriving on his new challenge,' he added, as if reading her mind. 'He's always been an efficient, dedicated engineer, and now he's proving to be an equally efficient, dedicated plant manager.'

'You saw him?'

'Of course.' He raised a sardonic eyebrow. 'Why. . . are you missing him?' The black eyes narrowed slightly, searching hers.

She flipped back her hair with a careless hand, somehow meeting his gaze without wavering. 'I don't have to be missing David to want to know how he's doing. I still care about him.'

Case nodded, a satisfied tilt to his lip. 'Then you'll be pleased to hear he's in excellent spirits, by all accounts. In fact...I heard he's been seeing quite a bit of Sally. You remember Sally?'

'Of course.' Lucy jutted her chin. 'You wouldn't be trying to make me jealous, would you?'

A mocking glint lit his eye. 'You never wanted David...why should I try to make you jealous?' He waved her out as the lift reached ground level. 'I just thought you'd be pleased to hear he's not pining away for you.'

'I am pleased.' And no doubt you're feeling equally pleased with yourself, Case Travers, she thought, with a spurt of resentment at his high-handed way of taking over people's lives. By transferring David to Sydney, he'd virtually thrown Sally and David together.

Was that what he'd been hoping would happen?

As he steered her across the soaring lobby to the street she found her thoughts going haywire. She recalled how she'd once fleetingly wondered, before dismissing the thought, if Case had sent David to Sydney to clear the way for himself. Was it possible she'd been close to the truth all along? Would a man as hard-nosed and cynical as Case Travers go to such lengths? Put his heart, his needs, his desires, ahead of his family company to get a woman he wanted? A deep quiver ran through her.

If Case *did* want her. For whatever reason.

And, of course, what Case Travers wanted, Case Travers would expect to get. The Case Traverses of this world were accustomed to getting whatever they wanted. Women in particular.

By now they were heading along Collins Street. It was already dark and the plane trees lining

Melbourne's most elegant street were twinkling with tiny gold lights. Case took her to Max's at the Hyatt for dinner. It was very swish, very up-market, and she was thankful he'd warned her that he was taking her out to dinner, and that she'd worn her cherry-red suit to town. A few other elegantly dressed diners sat at a discreet distance, conversing in low voices.

'I've made the bookings for Saturday,' Case told her as their prawn cocktails arrived. 'Our plane leaves at midday. I'll pick you up at ten-thirty, to allow for Saturday morning traffic. You've told your mother you're coming?'

He hadn't even bothered to ask if his plans were acceptable. Of course not. He wouldn't. She faced him mutinously, stifling a tremor that rippled through her as she realised he still intended to come. She'd half expected him to make some excuse to back out. As it was, his gaze was curiously shuttered again, impossible to read.

'Yes,' she said briefly, trying to keep her own expression as inscrutable as his.

'You didn't mention to her that I was coming with you?'

'No.' She sighed. 'Since you asked me not to.'

'Good,' he said equably, and changed the subject.

They'd both chosen the poached veal for their main course. It was delicious. When their plates had been whisked away, Case asked with a coaxing smile, 'Like to see the dessert menu?'

She shook her head. 'Just coffee for me, thanks.' She felt more in need of some strong coffee than any more food. Anything to settle the butterflies inside her, the doubts that still lingered. 'How about you?'

'Not for me. Look. . .let's have coffee back at my place.' He was already waving a finger for the bill. 'I'll need you to give me a lift home anyway. I took my car in for a service this morning, and it won't be ready until tomorrow. You did bring your car in, didn't you?'

She nodded, her heart missing a beat. Coffee...at his place? Would Jean and Bill be there? Or had Case given them the night off? Did he think the time had come to step things up a bit, make his move on her, without even waiting to check out her mother and her background first?

'Thanks.' He took her nod as agreement. 'It'll save me calling a cab.' As the bill was handed to him she slipped out to the ladies' room and took a few long, deep breaths to calm herself down. Some fresh lipstick and a dab of powder helped give her some much needed moral armour. She had a feeling she might need it shortly, the way her body was warring with her mind.

Half an hour later she was swinging her car into Case's tree-lined driveway. The front porch lights of his house were on, but the rest of the house was in total darkness. Jean and Bill were either away, or they'd already retired for the night.

She gulped hard as she brought her car to a halt near the wide front steps. 'Are you sure you want me to come in?' She felt suddenly, ridiculously nervous. 'I wouldn't want to disturb Jean and Bill at this hour.'

'It's not late.' He sounded amused, as if he sensed her inner turmoil and found it...quaint. 'And we won't be disturbing Jean and Bill. They'll be in their own wing at the back of the house. I told them I wouldn't be needing them.'

Her throat went dry. So...he'd warned them to keep out of the way, had he? So they wouldn't be likely to walk in on them unexpectedly? She felt a shivery thrill down her spine. Whatever Case was planning or hoping to do, would she be capable of saying no? Would she *want* to?

She felt another tingly shiver, knowing in her heart that she wouldn't. But she had to! Feeling the way she did about him, to give in to him, a man who didn't love her, would be asking for trouble.

But she *wanted* Case. . .wanted him as she had never wanted any man before. Life was full of risks. And if he wanted *her*. . .even if he didn't intend to keep her in his life for long. . .

Maybe, just maybe, if she gave in to him now—and gave him a taste in the nights ahead of what real loving could be like, showed him how good it could be—a miracle would happen and he wouldn't *want* to give her up?

Did miracles happen to unworldly suburban podiatrists?

Case led her through to the kitchen. After removing his jacket and throwing it over the back of a chair he set about preparing the coffee, in a briskly efficient manner that showed he was used to the task.

Used to bringing women home late at night?

Lucy stifled the thought, determined not to let his other women bother her. Not tonight. It wasn't as if they'd meant anything to him. . .he'd said so himself.

He must have some feeling for her. 'I care more about what you think of me,' he'd told her. It wasn't quite the same thing as saying, I care about *you*, but it came close. She preferred not to think about the way he'd stiffened and withdrawn after he'd said it. He was wary of commitment, wary of putting his heart in the hands of another woman. It was understandable, after what he'd been through.

If she could show him, prove to him that she was different from the other women he'd known since his divorce. . .that all women were not like his wife. . .

'Sorry. Thanks,' she mumbled when she realised he was holding out a mug of coffee for her to take. He waved her into the family room, where the gas fire was burning, flames licking warmly in the deep red glow.

As they sat sipping their coffee Case said casually, 'Afraid I'll have to miss my swim in the morning. John's picking me up very early for a pre-breakfast meeting in town. But you must still come, Lucy. And tomorrow night I have a business function, so I won't be able to see you again until I pick you up on Saturday morning.'

He slanted his head at her. 'Why don't you use some of your consultancy cheque to buy yourself a new dress for your mother's birthday? I have a hankering to see you in plain, classic black. Or do you already have a little black dress?'

She flicked the tip of her tongue over her lips. There was something in his eyes now. . .something soft, warm. Dangerous. Dangerous to her senses. 'I do, as it happens.' She cleared her throat as she heard the betraying huskiness in her voice. 'I'd already decided to wear it on Saturday night as a matter of fact. So. . . I don't really need a new dress. I'd rather use the cheque to help pay off my car.'

She hadn't even opened his envelope yet, she realised. She had no idea how much Case had given her. At least it must cover the cost of a new dress. Knowing Case, an *expensive* dress.

'I thought all women needed a new dress. . .whenever the chance presented itself.' The bantering light still lurked in his eyes. And then it changed to something else, something that started her heart beating wildly. 'But then. . .you're not *all women*, are you, Lucy?'

She raised her chin, hiding her inner turmoil behind a flash of spirit that intensified the blue of her eyes. 'I'm still a woman. I like shopping for a new dress if I need one. But just at the moment I can put the money to better use.'

'Well, let's hope you'll like what I have for you, new dress or not.' Case rose as he spoke.

Lucy watched, suddenly wary, as he strode over to the mantelpiece and plucked a small box from the shelf. A black velvet-covered box, she noted as he swung back and stood over her. A *jewel* box?

Her body stiffened, her senses leaping to full alert.

'Open it,' he invited, holding it out to her. He was smiling now, a benign, complacent smile.

'You open it,' she said shakily, making no move to take it.

'All right.' Case opened the box and held it out so that she could see what was inside.

When she said nothing—she'd gone quite still, her tongue locked in her throat—he said quietly, 'I hope you like it, Lucy. I've always believed that lovely neck of yours needs adornment of some kind. The right adornment. . .'

She stared. It was stunning. The most exquisite necklace she'd ever seen, with tiny pearls so smooth, so glowing, so perfect they took her breath away, and other smaller gems glistening between the pearls. Surely nothing could glisten that way but. . .diamonds!

Her heard jerked back.

'It's for you.' Case's smile inched wider. 'I hope you'll wear it to your mother's birthday dinner on Saturday night, Lucy, with your little black— What's wrong?' he asked sharply.

She'd drawn in her breath, not attempting to hide the hurt, the fierce rejection in her eyes. Then anger overrode the hurt. This was plainly a softener, a pay-off, before he backed out of her life. Stupid fool that she was! Case Travers had never wanted her. He'd never even wanted an *affair*! He'd only wanted to pick her brains, to use her.

And now that he had he was easing himself out of her life. . .with offers of plane trips to Queensland to visit her mother. . .with glitzy birthday dinners. . .with expensive gifts. He'd see Saturday night through— though why he'd still want to fly to Brisbane with her she couldn't imagine, unless it was to make sure that she was in her mother's care when he dumped her— and then he'd be off and out of her life for good.

'I know what you're thinking.' Case's voice rumbled above her. He sounded *amused*, damn him! 'It's what I

said about jewelled parting gifts, isn't it? Well, this is
not a parting gift, Lucy. . .far from it. I want to keep
you in my life. . .one way or another.'

Lucy stopped breathing, her heart almost jumping
out of her chest. What did he mean by 'one way or
another'? Was he asking her to be his lover—his
mistress—but telling her that if she wouldn't agree to
that, he'd still want her in his life. . .as a friend?

Did men like Case Travers make friends of surbur-
ban working girls? *Platonic* friends? The thought would
have made her laugh if she hadn't felt so upset and
confused. And suspicious.

She didn't take the necklace from him, didn't even
touch it.

'You don't need to offer inducements,' she said,
forcing a lightness edged with cool irony into her voice,
'to keep me as a. . .friend.' Let him spell it out, if he
wanted more.

'Is that all you want to be to me, Lucy? A friend?'

She forced her gaze not to flinch under his. Oh, no,
you're not going to trap me that way, Case Travers, she
thought. No doubt he was used to his women prostrat-
ing themselves at his feet, begging him to take them
into his arms, into his bed. . .hoping desperately for
more.

As she wavered he said, 'You still can't bring yourself
to trust me, can you, Lucy?' He sounded pained. 'It
seems my fast and loose lifestyle since my divorce has
given you the wrong impression of me.' He gave a
rueful smile. 'I assure you, Lucy, the necklace is not an
inducement. There's no ulterior motive behind it. It's
just an expression of. . .' did he hesitate for a second?
'. . .the way I feel about you. Please take it. Wear it.
Enjoy it. Let's not make a big thing of it.'

But he still wasn't telling her precisely *how* he felt
about her. . .or what he wanted from her! He didn't
even seem to want to take her in his arms and
show her.

What was holding him back? The memory of his ex-wife? The painful scars, the heartache his wife had caused him? He must have had feelings for her as well. . .at one time.

'I'm sorry, Case,' she said heavily. 'I can't take it. But thank you. It was. . .a generous thought.' She flicked back her soft hair with a toss of her head, valiantly hiding the pain in her heart. 'I'd better be going.' She slipped from her chair and wove her way past him.

He didn't try to stop her. That more than anything convinced her that he had no intention of offering her what *she* wanted more than anything else in the world. A piece of himself. A piece of his heart.

But out in the chill night air, just as she reached her car, he caught up with her, grabbing her arm from behind and swinging her round to face him.

'Don't go like this, Lucy. . .' There was a raw edge to his voice, an almost anguished note that shook her, brought her head up sharply. 'You must know by now how I feel about you. . .' His fingers dug into her flesh so tightly that she almost cried out. 'Just give me time. . .a few days. . .please.'

A few *days*? She looked up at him, her blue eyes widening, swirling with chaotic emotions, hurt and resentment uppermost. She'd never known Case Travers to be indecisive, not to know his own mind. Obviously he didn't want her. . .not really. He was fighting his feelings. Whatever they were.

Anything she might have said or tried to say was stifled by his mouth, his heated lips capturing hers in a hungry assault on her senses. His arms were like a vice around her, almost bending her over backwards, his body strong and hard-muscled, crushing into her soft curves. Breathy sounds escaped her as his mouth plundered hers in one savage kiss after another, igniting a fierce heat in her that seemed to explode, pouring hot liquid into every corner of her body.

She knew she should be fighting him, or at least fighting the feelings exploding inside her, but she was helpless, resistance beyond her control. She moaned beneath the continuing onslaught, moaned and melted, her knees threatening to give way beneath her. Only the strength of his supporting arms saved her from sinking to the gravel path at his feet.

Endless as it seemed, it was over in seconds. With a stifled groan he wrenched his mouth from hers, his head lifting, his black eyes blazing down at her, two bright gleams in the darkness. 'You'd better go while you have the chance!' he bit out, his breath rasping, his body seeming to shudder as he clasped her to his chest for a fierce moment, pressing her hot cheek into his shirt.

The brief respite gave her a chance to catch her breath, to regain some strength in her rubbery legs. She could hear his heart thumping erratically against her ear, as if she'd aroused him as much as he had her. She gave a trembling sigh, wondering why, if he wanted her as much as he appeared to want her, he was urging her to go.

Was it because he'd sensed how deeply she felt about *him*, when all he wanted from her was a sizzling, short-lived affair? Had it struck him, just in time, that she was never going to be able to play by his rules and let go when the time came? She felt her throat constrict. Was that why he'd been holding back? Because he'd sensed that she was different from his other, more hard-boiled, sophisticated conquests, a naïve, old-fashioned romantic in need of the kid glove approach, and so had deliberately not rushed her, hoping that if he took his time he'd eventually get her into his bed. . . on his terms? *Easy come, easy go.* And now, suddenly, was he having second thoughts about taking the risk?

As the doubts swirled through her he released her abruptly, reaching out in a lightning movement to open the door of her car.

'See you Saturday morning.' His voice was thick, hoarse. With thwarted desire? Or. . .relief? 'Ten-thirty.'

'I'll be ready,' she said unsteadily as she sank weakly behind the wheel and with fumbling fingers turned the key in the ignition. As the engine revved in the night silence she put her foot down hard. She thought she heard him call out, 'Drive safely,' as the car lurched forward, but she didn't look back. She wouldn't have seen him anyway, with her eyes blurred with tears.

CHAPTER TEN

ALL the way to Brisbane, from the moment Case had picked her up and driven her to Melbourne Airport to the moment they'd arrived at Avril and her mother's bungalow-style home in the Ford Fairlane they'd hired at Brisbane Airport, Case seemed restless, tense, unusually taciturn, as if impatient to get there. Impatient to get it over with?

Lucy glanced up at him as they walked from the car to the lush vine-clad veranda shading the front of the house. Was he regretting that he'd ever suggested coming to Brisbane with her?

It was her mother who answered the door. Charlotte saw Lucy first, holding out a huge bunch of delicate pink roses, which they'd stopped to buy on the way.

'Happy birthday, Mum.'

'Darling, it's so good to see you! And what lovely roses. They smell wonderful.' As she darted forward to take the flowers and give her daughter a hug Charlotte saw Case standing behind her, Lucy's overnight bag in his hand.

She stiffened.

'Oh, Mum. . .this is Case Travers.' Lucy tried to keep her tone light. 'He flew up for the weekend too. He's been. . .keen to meet you.'

'To meet me?' Charlotte echoed sharply, her expression wary as she eyed the man behind.

'Mrs Farrell. . .' Stepping forward, Case found himself staring into a pair of blue eyes that at one time must have been as startlingly blue as her daughter's, though the years—or pain—had robbed them of the brilliant lustre they must once have had, as time also dimmed her beauty and vitality.

But it was plain that Charlotte, in her youth, would have been the spitting image of her daughter. She was still a handsome woman, though, looking more closely, Case perceived an inner sadness, a remoteness about her that her daughter thankfully lacked.

'May I wish you a happy birthday, Mrs Farrell?' He extended a hand which Charlotte accepted guardedly and was quick to relinquish. 'Your daughter has been doing some consulting work for me. . .as she must have told you. She's been invaluable. Knows instinctively what I want.' He paused, then added smoothly, 'Lucy and I have become good friends in these past weeks. We have a lot in common, we've found.'

Lucy's eyes leapt to his, her heart turning over. 'A lot in common'? she echoed silently as he paused again, as if waiting for her mother's reaction. She eyed him narrowly. Was he deliberately taunting her mother, knowing that Charlotte disapproved of him? Or was he saying what he sincerely believed to be the truth? 'Good friends. . .a lot in common. . .'

We do get on well, she mused, her eyes turning pensive. I have more in common with Case—leaving aside our backgrounds and lifestyles—than I ever had with David.

'You're staying in Brisbane too, Mr Travers?' Charlotte asked, a marked frostiness edging the polite question.

'Just for tonight, yes. I've booked a room at the Sheraton, where, with your daughter's permission, I've already reserved a table for dinner this evening.' Case flashed a smile that would have melted most women. 'I'm hoping you will permit me to join you for your birthday celebration, Mrs Farrell. . .as your host?'

'You don't mind, do you, Mum?' Lucy asked quickly, afraid that her mother might make some excuse to avoid having his presence thrust on them. Case, for his part, was going all out to charm her mother. How could Charlotte resist?'

'Oh, Lottie, the Sheraton! How lovely!' cried a tinkling voice from behind. 'It's not often these days we have a posh five-star dinner, dear! Lucy, love. . . how *are* you?'

'Avril, dear. . .' Charlotte turned her head. 'You must meet our. . .visitor.' She waved a careless hand. 'Case Travers. . .Avril Davies. Lucy has been doing some consulting work for Mr Travers,' she told her old friend, to explain his presence.

'Please, call me Case.' His smile flashed again as Avril, releasing Lucy from a warm embrace, leapt forward to pump his hand. A tall, big-boned woman, she had a round, girlish face and an equally girlish voice that belied her sixty-odd years.

Case switched his charm to Avril for a moment, before turning back to Charlotte. 'Am I permitted to call you Avril and Charlotte? Or. . .is it Lottie you prefer, Mrs Farrell?'

Lottie? He doesn't miss a trick, Lucy thought in silent admiration at the way he'd picked up her mother's nickname. But nobody called her mother Lottie but Avril. Charlotte detested the name and wouldn't permit it. She only tolerated it from Avril because her old friend had called her Lottie at school and throughout their respective marriages, and had refused to change when Charlotte had moved up to Brisbane to live with her.

'Avril and Charlotte will do nicely,' her mother told Case frigidly. 'Well, are you coming in?' she asked, her eyes flicking back to Lucy.

'I won't, thanks.' It was Case who answered, and there was a faint edge to his voice now. Understandably, Lucy thought with an inward sigh, the way her mother was treating him. 'I'm sure you and your daughter have a lot to catch up on, Charlotte, before your birthday dinner tonight. I want to check in at the hotel and make sure we have a good table for tonight. Pick you up at seven. . .does that sound OK?'

Charlotte nodded, giving him a tight little smile. Lucy felt like kicking her mother for making it so obvious that she didn't want him here or approve of his barging in on her birthday dinner in what she obviously considered a high-handedly arrogant manner. No wonder Case's own smile was starting to look a bit forced.

The moment Case drove off Lucy snatched up her bag and turned on her mother, demanding fractiously, 'Just what is it precisely that you have against Case Travers? You're not normally so rude to people.'

Her mother had the grace to blush. But before she could come up with an answer, Avril grabbed the roses from Charlotte's hand. 'I'll put these in a vase for you, dear, and then make you a cup of tea,' she said, and scurried off.

'Well?' Lucy pressed, glaring at her mother.

Charlotte sighed and drew her inside, closing the door behind them. 'It's nothing personal. . .I suppose. I don't even know the man. But I do know his type.' Her lips tightened. 'Men like Case Travers think their money and power can buy anything. . .and anyone. They know how to sweep a girl off her feet and fool her into thinking they truly care. . .even into believing it's going to last. But it never does, Lucy. Believe me. This man has had one broken marriage already, remember.'

Lucy's eyes turned stormy. 'You know nothing about his marriage or why it failed!' She dropped her bag on the floor and faced her mother with clenched fists, all her doubts about Case dissolving in her need to defend him.

'*I* understand why it failed, and it had nothing to do with Case being fickle, or being a particular *type*. It was his *wife* who wasn't cut out for marriage—or not for the kind of marriage and family life that Case wanted. Case was the one who wanted to settle down and have children. He was devastated when it didn't work out.

His own parents' marriage lasted happily for forty-odd years. Case's *father* was rich and powerful too, yet no breath of scandal ever touched *him*, despite his wealth and lifestyle. So please. . .get to know Case before you talk about *types*!'

Charlotte, standing tensely in front of her, turned away so abruptly that Lucy gave a cry of concern. 'Mum. . .what is it? What have I said?'

Her mother didn't seem able to look at her. 'Nothing,' she said tightly. 'No. . .you're right, dear. I'm being silly. I'm overreacting. But promise me, darling. . .you will be careful? You won't expect. . .too much?'

'Mum. . .I'm not,' Lucy said, and heard the bleak yearning in her voice. 'I don't believe Case is over his wife yet. Or ready to fully trust another woman.' She sighed, then admitted in a rush, 'I know there's something stopping him getting too close to—to anyone.'

'To you, you mean?' Charlotte asked gently, concern in her eyes.

Lucy gulped, and shook her head. 'No. . .he doesn't want to get too close to *me*.' She lifted her chin. 'It's understandable, isn't it? Considering he's who he is and the fact that we don't exactly move in the same circles? We're worlds apart, Mum. So you don't have to worry. I have my eyes w-wide open.' To her horror, her voice broke as she said it, and tears sprang to her eyes. As she tried furiously to blink them away her mother gathered her in her arms.

'Oh, my dear. . . My poor baby! You've fallen in love with him. . .haven't you?'

Lucy heaved a shuddering sigh. What was the point in denying it any longer? To herself or to her mother? 'I. . .c-couldn't help it,' she choked. 'He's—he's everything to me, Mum. I never felt like this with David. I never believed I could feel like this with anyone. But d-don't worry, Mum.' She tossed her head, her lips trembling. 'I'm not expecting too much. I'm not expecting anything. . .honestly. B-but—' she gave a muffled sob '—I can still dream, can't I?'

'Oh, my dear!' Charlotte held her close. 'I wish I could say something that would help. But I can't. I knew a man once. . .so like Case.'

Lucy raised blurred eyes to hers. 'You. . .did? You're saying you. . .you had an *affair*?' Had Case's stab in the dark been right all along? 'Did. . .Dad know?' she asked tentatively.

'Oh, darling, it was long before your father came into my life.' Charlotte forced a smile, but it was the saddest smile Lucy had ever seen. 'You know I would never have done that to Martin. . . Though in a way,' she added with a sigh, 'it was as if I had. He knew there'd been someone else, you see. Someone I'd cared deeply about, and who had. . .hurt me badly. I'm sure that's why he turned to Beth after all those years. She gave him something I was never able to. Something I'd had myself once. . .or thought I'd had.

'I stupidly believed it was mutual, you see. That he felt the same. But—' her voice wobbled and turned bitter '—it was an illusion. And illusions never last. Now you know, darling, why I've always told you to be very sure before making a commitment to any man. If you're not, neither of you will ever be completely happy. . .no matter how hard you try. And it won't last.'

'Mum, who was it?' Lucy breathed. 'This man you once loved?'

Her mother shook her head, her eyes shadowed with pain. 'It doesn't matter now. It was a long time ago. . . a lifetime ago. Anyway, I promised him I'd never tell a living soul, and I never have. I never saw him again after he went back to his wife.'

Lucy's head jerked up. 'He was *married*?'

'Please. . .' Charlotte eyes were stricken. 'I don't want to talk about it. I'm too ashamed. I just want to forget it.'

'Oh, Mum, I wasn't judging you. I was just surprised, that's all,' Lucy cried in distress. 'I'm glad you told me. I understand now. . .a lot of things.'

About her mother. About why her parents' marriage hadn't lasted the distance. And why her father, after all those years, had turned to another woman. Her mother's love affair, back in the dim past though it had been, had haunted them, blighted their lives. . .and ultimately destroyed their marriage.

'Mum. . .please give Case a chance,' she begged. 'Please try to meet him halfway tonight. Make an effort to get to know him better. I'd be really pleased if you could come to—to like him. Whatever happens in the future.'

Her mother gave her a squeeze. 'I'll try, dear, I promise. And thank you, darling, for being so under-standing. . .for listening to your foolish mother.'

'I love you, Mum.' Lucy pressed her lips to her mother's cheek. 'Let's find Avril, shall we? I could do with that cup of tea.'

Case arrived on the dot of seven. As Lucy opened the front door she felt his eyes searching her face, sensed the tightly coiled tension in him. What was he looking for? Was he afraid that Charlotte might have warned her to stay away from him? Might even have succeeded in turning her against him?

Why, Lucy wondered in bewilderment, would her mother's opinions matter to him so much? To a man so used to making his own decisions. . .to making things happen. . .even to running people's lives?

Seeing the visible strain in his face, seeing that he could be vulnerable and uncertain too, that he didn't always have the answer to everything was strangely moving. And heartening. She felt her spirits lift.

Suddenly wanting to boost his spirits too, she gave him her most dazzling smile. And at once she saw the tension slide from his face, as if her smile had reassured him in some way.

His answering smile was like a flash of sunlight, wiping the hard lines from his face. 'You look lovely, Lucy.' His eyes skimmed over her little black dress and along the bare, unadorned slenderness of her neck, his smile turning wry as he asked, 'Your mother is reconciled to having me come along?'

'I'm sure you'll find that she is,' Lucy said, stepping out onto the veranda, where the warm, sultry air, even at this hour of the evening, swirled round them like a blanket. Nobody would need coats tonight. Not in this balmy heat. It was hard to believe it was winter. Back home in Melbourne she'd been wearing warm woollies for weeks. 'They're just locking up.'

'You and your mother had a good chat this afternoon?' Case asked as they stood waiting, and though his tone held a mildly teasing note, his eyes were hooded again.

'A very good chat,' she assured him, raising clear blue eyes to his to set his mind at rest. Had he truly been worried about her mother warning her off? 'Ah. . .here they are now,' she said.

Case had secured the best table at the Sheraton's classiest restaurant. The finest French champagne sat chilling in a silver ice bucket—though Case didn't force it on them, asking first if they'd like champagne or would prefer something else. Nobody declined. After toasting Charlotte and wishing her well, they turned their attention to the extensive dinner menu.

Case was the perfect host—attentive, charming and witty, conversing easily throughout the superb meal without monopolising the conversation, gently drawing comments from each of them, keeping the talk flowing and full of interest and at the same time avoiding intrusive personal questions.

The evening flew by, and in no time, it seemed, it

was over. Replete, after rounding off their meal with coffee and chocolates, they headed back to Avril's in the hired Fairlane, the Brisbane River, silvery in the soft moonlight, meandering alongside them.

'Will you come in for a nightcap?' Lucy asked as Case escorted them to Avril's front door. 'You'll have one, won't you, Mum? Avril?' She wanted the evening to last...to go on for ever. As long as Case was there to share it. She'd decided over dinner not to fight her feelings any more. Case was the man she wanted, and, impossible as a future with him seemed, she wasn't going to give up and back away.

'Not for me, thanks,' Charlotte said with a quick smile. There was no sign of her earlier coolness—in fact she'd been back to her usual warm self all evening, burying whatever reservations she might still have about Case. 'After all that food and wine I'm ready for my bed. But by all means come in, Case... Lucy knows where the drinks are. I'll just thank you for a lovely evening, and say goodnight. It was most enjoyable.'

'Just wonderful,' Avril trilled. 'I'll toddle off too... it's way past my bedtime. Thank you, Case, for a great night. Goodnight, dear.' She gave Lucy a swift peck on the cheek.

Lucy was grateful to them. They were letting her have some time alone with Case. Not that they'd be as alone as she would have liked. The walls of Avril's home weren't all that thick!

'Thanks...but I won't come in,' Case declined, causing her heart to plummet. 'I'll leave you all to get your beauty sleep. But if you're agreeable, Charlotte,' he added as Lucy's mother was about to step away, 'I'd like to drop in tomorrow morning and spend some more time with you all before Lucy and I head off to the airport. May I drop in around eleven-thirty? I won't intrude before then.'

'Well, yes, of course...drop in whenever you like.' Charlotte, pausing, looked surprised that Case should want to spend any more time with them—with two elderly women—when he could have been doing something else on his own, or whisking Lucy off somewhere, since they were up here for such a short time.

He's being considerate. . .giving Mum extra time with me, Lucy thought, still disappointed that he hadn't agreed to stay a bit longer tonight, when they could have been alone, just the two of them. Didn't he *want* to be alone with her?

Or—her heart flew to her mouth—was it that he felt they wouldn't be alone *enough*?

She said goodnight to him on the front veranda, and his lingering kiss before he left her was as tender, as passionate, as reassuring as she could have wished, dissolving her nagging doubts.

Except that she wished it could have been more.

He left without saying anything more than, 'See you in the morning, Lucy.' But the look he gave her as he swung away, and the way his fingers almost crushed hers before he abruptly let them go, seemed to be telling her that he wished it could have been more too.

CHAPTER ELEVEN

CASE arrived at eleven-thirty, as promised. Lucy felt a twinge of guilt when she realised she'd hardly heard a thing her mother or Avril had said to her all morning. Her mind had been on Case, on seeing him again, on looking for that tenderness in his eyes that she'd glimpsed last night. She'd kept one eye on the clock, all her senses bristlingly alert, straining for the sound of his car, his footsteps, his knock on the door.

Those sounds had finally come.

'Case, good morning!' she smiled brightly as she threw open the door.

'Good morning, Lucy.' With a smile he bent his head and kissed her, but it was her cheek he kissed this time, not her mouth. He seemed different this morning, more serious, his manner tense again, preoccupied. A sudden fear gripped her. She'd never been a particularly psychic person, the type to have premonitions, but in that moment she had the strongest, weirdest, most ominous sensation that something bad was about to happen.

'Case. . .is there something wrong?' She had to know. She couldn't bear this suspense, the not knowing, the nagging fear.

Something gleamed in his black eyes. He seemed startled that she'd noticed anything amiss.

'Sorry. . .you know me too well.' He gave a grimace. 'I do have something on my mind. . .something that needs to be. . .resolved,' he admitted, and added quickly, 'But it's nothing to worry about.' His hand closed over her arm in a quick squeeze. 'Whatever happens, it will be all right, Lucy. . . I'll see that it is.' But he didn't convince her. 'May I come in?' he asked.

'Yes. . .of course.' Her voice had gone hoarse, sounding unlike her own. She led him inside, her legs feeling stiff and unnatural as she placed one foot in front of the other.

Charlotte came to meet him, her face smiling up into his. 'We had a lovely time last night, Case. It was a birthday to remember. Avril has just gone to put the kettle on. Please. . .won't you sit down?'

Case shook his head. 'I'm fine. . .thank you.' His chest heaved as he drew in a deep breath. 'I have something to give you, Charlotte. Something I'd like you to have.'

Lucy, watching him closely, could feel the fierce tension in him, though he was hiding it well, even smiling. But to her his smile seemed stiff, lacking the easy charm of yesterday. As he dug into his pocket and pulled out a small square velvet-covered box she caught her breath. Was he offering her *mother* a piece of jewellery now—as a belated birthday gift? Was that why he was acting so oddly? Because he was afraid Charlotte might refuse to accept it. . .as her daughter had refused to accept his diamond and pearl necklace?

But he'd talked about *resolving* something. Was this—whatever the box held—some kind of sweetener before he got down to the business he wanted resolved? Like—she gulped, her mind spinning into fantasyland—like asking her mother if she'd mind having him, a man who'd already been married and divorced once, permanently in her daughter's life?

She almost laughed aloud at the notion, at the same time releasing a trembling sigh from her lips. If that wasn't wishful thinking. . .! To say nothing of sheer madness. If Case wanted her—or any woman—in his life, nothing and nobody would stop him. He was that kind of man.

Case opened the jewel box and held it out to her mother, his eyes on her face. In a kind of numbed shock, Lucy saw her mother recoil as if stung, the blood draining from her cheeks.

'You'd better sit down, Charlotte,' Case said quickly, offering a supporting hand as Charlotte sank wordlessly into the nearest chair.

'Show me,' Lucy whispered, her throat constricting. Case, glancing round at her with an enigmatic expression, held out the box so she could see.

Inside was an exquisitely crafted antique brooch fashioned into the shape of the letter L. It was encrusted with beautiful gems which looked suspiciously like real rubies and emeralds.

Lucy's brow puckered in confusion. Why would Case give her mother an old brooch, no matter how valuable or beautiful, which had clearly been made for someone whose name started with the letter L?

'You've seen this before, Charlotte. . .haven't you?' Case asked quietly.

Charlotte sat like stone. Only the tip of her tongue moved, flicking over her pale lips. 'Why are you giving this to me,' she demanded, rallying, 'and not Lucy? Her name starts with L, not mine.'

'Perhaps the person who had this brooch made was in the habit of calling you. . .Lottie?' Case suggested gently.

Lucy saw the stricken look in her mother's eyes and ran to her side. 'Mum, what's wrong?' She looked up sharply. 'Case, what's going on? Can't you see you're upsetting my mother?'

'I'm sorry, Lucy,' Case muttered. His face was taut, the skin over his strong cheekbones stretched tight. 'But I have to ask. Please, Charlotte,' he pressed.

Charlotte jerked a look up at him, her lips tightening, yet betrayed by a quiver. She had a deathly pallor, her blue eyes stark in her face. 'Avril is the only person who calls me Lottie,' she said stiffly. 'Anyway, what in the world makes you think I might have seen this before, let alone imagine it might have been made for me? Where did you get it?' she demanded in a husky whisper.

'I found it in my father's safe after he died,' Case said, his eyes fixed to her face. 'It was in a small metal box with a combination lock. The combination was in a sealed envelope addressed to me, with a note to dispose of the contents of the box if my father died before. . .my mother. He didn't; they died together in a plane crash. If my father had outlived my mother, perhaps he might have tried to find you himself.'

'Find me?' Charlotte echoed hoarsely. 'What are you talking about? Why would your father have wanted to find *me*? And what makes you think this brooch has anything to do with me?' Her blue eyes flared suddenly. 'Was there. . .something else in the box?'

'There was, as it happens.' Case's eyes seemed to soften, though the tension was still in his face, in the deep lines gashing his cheeks. 'A photograph.'

He reached into his pocket again and pulled out a coloured snapshot, the kind of amateur shot that any-one might take. 'This is what led me to you, Charlotte,' he said, showing it to her. 'By an amazing coincidence, I met your daughter in town one day. . .quite by accident. And I found myself looking at the very same face as the face in this photograph. But I knew it couldn't be a photo of Lucy, because it was old and dated long before she was even born. I guessed it could only have been her mother. . .especially when Lucy told me she was the image of her mother at the same age.'

Lucy bit back a gasp as she peered down at the snapshot in his hand and saw a mirror image of herself. A young girl with wide-set turquoise eyes and smooth chestnut hair, her face glowingly alive, her full lips parted in a dazzling smile and eyes brimming over with happiness and what could only be. . .love. It was her mother at around the same age as she was now. She'd seen similar photos—without this enraptured look—in the family albums at home.

'Your father kept my photograph. . .all this time?' Charlotte asked shakily. 'Why—why would he do that?'

'You obviously meant a great deal to him,' Case said, a heaviness in his voice now. Was he thinking of his own mother now, the woman his father had been married to, supposedly happily, for forty-odd years? 'And he must have meant a lot to you too, Charlotte, at one time. . .judging by the words scrawled across the bottom of the photograph.'

He held it so that Lucy and her mother could read the words, handwritten in fading black ink: 'For my darling Nicholas, with all my love for ever, Lottie.' It was dated the third of September, thirty-five years ago.

Charlotte seemed to sag in her chair. As Lucy bent over her an awful realisation hit her. Her eyes flashed to Case.

'So this is why you were so keen to get to know me!' Her voice was a painful croak. 'You were determined to track down the mystery woman in your father's photograph. . .determined to find out what she'd meant to him, *been* to him, and why he'd kept her photograph all these years.'

She raised hurt, reproachful eyes to his, her heart dying inside her. 'No wonder you kept asking questions about my mother. No wonder you were so anxious to meet her. No wonder you wanted to go on seeing *me*. What quicker, easier way to get to my mother?'

She jerked her head away to hide the total devastation she was feeling inside. He'd made her fall in love with him. . .he'd even pretended to have feelings for *her*. . .and all the time he hadn't wanted her or cared for her at all; he'd only wanted to find and confront her mother—to satisfy his own sick curiosity. He was as ruthless, as manipulative, as hard-hearted as she'd always suspected!

Before Case could speak—if indeed he had any intention of uttering a word in his own defence—Charlotte's head snapped up. Eyes blazing, she let loose a tongue-lashing of her own.

'See what you've done? See how you've hurt my

daughter? How *could* you use her like this? Using her to get to me! I was right to warn her against you. You're beneath contempt! Men like you—and, yes, your father too—don't care who you hurt as long as *your* lives are not affected, as long as you get whatever it is *you* want for as long as you want it! Why did you have to come? Why did you—?' Her voice cracked. 'Why did you have to dig up the past? It all happened years ago, a lifetime ago! It had nothing to do with you!'

'Charlotte, I'm sorry. The last thing I wanted was to cause you pain. . .or Lucy,' Case assured her at once. His face was still tight, his strong jaw clenched. 'But it's important to me.'

He leaned towards her, a softer gleam in his eyes. 'Doesn't it mean anything to you, Charlotte, that my father kept your photograph all these years? Kept it safe and secure, in a place where he could steal a look at it from time to time, and wish things could have been different? Doesn't it mean anything to you that he kept this brooch with your initial on it? Wouldn't you accept it? Was that why he never gave it to you?

'Please, Charlotte.' Compelling dark eyes appealed to her. 'Tell us what happened all those years ago. Tell us about your love affair with my father. I. . .need to know.'

'*Why* do you need to know?' Lucy slid a protective arm round her mother's shoulders. 'Can't you see what you're doing to my mother, raking up the past like this? What does it matter? It was so long ago! And it obviously didn't affect *your* parents' marriage. You've always said how happy your parents were. . .and what a wonderful family life you had.'

Charlotte reached for her hand. 'It's all right, darling,' she said, sighing. 'If he wants to know. . .he might as well know. Who can it hurt now? His parents have both gone, and I'm divorced from your father.' She glanced across the room as Avril appeared, halting at

the door as if reluctant to intrude. 'Come in, Avril.
You might as well hear this too. It certainly can't hurt
you.'

'It can hurt *you*, Mum,' Lucy cried. 'You don't have
to—'

'It's all right, dear. . . I want to.' Charlotte surprised
her with her words, her voice firmer now, colour
seeping back into her cheeks. 'Case is right. Knowing
that his father kept my photograph all these years, and
the brooch he wanted to give me, does mean a lot to
me. Maybe I meant more to him than I thought. He
always said I did, but when he—when he ended it so
abruptly and said we must never meet again, I—I
thought. . .' She shook her head, blinking rapidly.

'Mum, you don't have to—' Lucy began again, but
Charlotte patted her hand and hushed her.

'We did have an affair, Nicholas Travers and I,' she
admitted in a low voice. 'When we first met we were
attending the same finance seminar in Canberra—I
didn't know who he was at first, or that he was married,
or anything about him. It was. . .an instant thing. Overwhelming. For both of us. I know it sounds impous-
ible—' she gave a tremulous sigh '—but the moment
we met, something happened.

'It was beyond our control. I knew he was the one. . .
the only one for me. And he—he said he felt the same.
At the end of the seminar he told me he had to see me
again, and we learned that we actually worked in
adjoining office buildings back in Melbourne. We
began to meet. . .without anyone knowing.'

She kept her eyes downcast, fixed to the slender
hands in her lap. 'He'd told me by then that he was
married, that he'd been married for five years to his
childhood sweetheart. He said he and his wife had no
children, much as they both wanted them. It had been
causing strains on their marriage, driving a deep wedge
between them. His wife had taken up charity work to
keep herself occupied while he'd thrown himself into

his work, building up his paperboard business. He...'
she hesitated '...he told me he was going to ask his
wife for a divorce.'

Lucy sensed a stiffening in Case, but he said nothing.

'He—he told me he did still care for his wife, but
not—not the way he loved me.' Charlotte's mouth held
a bitter twist. 'You want to hear more?' she asked,
flicking a glance at Case. 'This must be as painful for
you as it is for me.'

'Please. Go on,' Case urged, his face shuttered,
unreadable.

Charlotte sighed. 'Nicholas said that if he and his
wife parted ways then, while they were both childless
and relatively young, they would have a chance to
make new lives for themselves...he with me, his wife
perhaps with someone else in time.

'But—' she twisted white-knuckled hands in her lap
'—on the very day that he planned to tell his wife about
me, and ask for a divorce, she—she told him that she
was pregnant, at last—that she was three months
already. She'd wanted to wait until she was perfectly
sure before she told him. She was ecstatic, over the
moon, he told me. Full of hope and happiness and
plans for the—the three of them.'

Charlotte bowed her head, her dark hair a curtain
round her face. 'He told me it was over...that he
couldn't leave her now. The child meant too much to
her...and to—to him. He said he wasn't going to let
his child be raised in a broken home, being torn two
ways, as he had been after his own parents divorced
when he was a child. He said that even though he—he
loved me and—and always would, we must never see
each other again.

'He made me promise never to speak about our
affair, ever. He couldn't risk his marriage now, he said,
couldn't risk losing his child, his family. And I—I
haven't spoken about it...until today. It can't hurt his

wife or his marriage now.' She raised moist, wistful eyes to Case. 'It can only hurt you. . .and Lucy.'

'Oh, Mum!' Lucy cried at once. '*You* haven't hurt me.' But Case had. By using her. . .by raking up the past to satisfy his own morbid curiosity. . .by exposing her mother to old, still raw wounds and forcing the painful truth from her. She hoped he *was* hurt!

'I'm hoping it will do precisely the opposite,' Case said levelly, his eyes on her mother's face. 'Charlotte, your break-up with my father was the reason, I take it, that you moved to Sydney all those years ago?'

As Charlotte nodded, her brow puckering, Lucy glared at him. Hadn't he caused her mother enough anguish already? Why was he persisting in dragging out every agonising detail?

'Your father said he couldn't bear to have me working in the building next to his. . .so close,' Charlotte told Case in a subdued voice. 'He offered to find me another job—a better one—out of the city somewhere, in the suburbs. I thought he just wanted to get rid of me so that he could forget about me. So I made it easy for him. I moved to Sydney. In fact, I left the business world altogether and found a finance job at a public hospital. It was there that I eventually met Martin, and grew to. . .love him, though not in the. . . never in quite the same way.'

Case loomed over her, his eyes intent on hers. 'And you didn't resume your affair with my father later? When he flew up to Sydney on business, perhaps—as he often did?'

'*Case!*' Lucy's furious yelp made him flinch, but he didn't retract.

'*Did* you, Charlotte?'

'No!' Charlotte cried raggedly. 'What are you trying to suggest now? That your father and I couldn't stay away from each other? That he still wanted to be my lover and I *allowed* it? I tell you, I never saw him again—ever. Not even when I was forced to move back to Melbourne later, when Martin's bank transferred us! I was always afraid, though, that one day I *might* bump into him.

'Why do you think I moved to Queensland when Lucy started going out with David? Because David worked for Maxi Board, and I thought that if Lucy decided to marry him David might invite *your father* to his wedding. Even after all those years, I—I couldn't bear the thought of coming face to face with Nicholas again.

'Then, after your parents were killed in that awful plane crash and Lucy met *you*, their son, I—I panicked. I even—I even lied about going away on that bus trip. I didn't want to meet you, Case. I didn't want Lucy getting tied up with anyone from Nicholas Travers' family. I—I thought it would be history repeating itself, that you wouldn't treat her seriously and she...she would end up badly hurt, the way I had been.'

'Me, *hurt*?' Lucy cried scathingly, though her heart was splintering inside. 'I'm incensed, not hurt!' She faced Case with a feeling close to hate. '*Now* are you satisfied? You know everything now. You've got what you wanted, what you got to know me for. I hope you're happy!'

Case straightened slowly and turned to her. He was actually smiling! 'I am happy,' he said. 'I'm very happy. You see...I had to be quite sure of something. I was fairly sure already...after yesterday. I was certain Charlotte would have told you last night, while she had the chance—or this morning—if what I'd half feared all along was true.'

'What are you talking about?' Lucy stared at him blankly. 'Sure of what?'

He looked down at her with his crooked, achingly attractive smile—an almost sheepish smile now. 'I had to be sure that you weren't my half-sister. That we didn't both share the same father!'

CHAPTER TWELVE

'YOU thought. . .*what*?' Lucy gaped at him.

'A dim possibility, I concede,' Case said calmly. The strain and tension of earlier had vanished from his face, miraculously wiped out. He looked totally at ease now, more so than she'd ever seen him. 'But I had to be sure there was nothing to stop me—' he glanced at her mother '—getting any closer to your daughter, Charlotte.' Again the corner of his mouth curved in that heart-melting smile. 'Am I forgiven for putting you through what I did?'

Charlotte pursed her lips. She wasn't going to let him off the hook so easily. 'You want to get closer to my daughter?' she asked, tilting her head at him. 'Just how close did you have in mind?'

'Mum!' Lucy chided. 'I *am* over twenty-one. I'll decide how close I'll let him get.' She felt an excited tremor run through her, her earlier hurt and fury forgotten.

So this was why Case had been so anxious to find out the truth about her mother's long-ago affair with his father, Nicholas Travers. . .why he'd never gone beyond a certain point with her. . .why she'd felt all along that there was something holding him back. It had had nothing to do with his failed marriage or a resistance to getting emotionally involved again. It had had nothing to do with their different backgrounds or lifestyles. He'd been worried that they might both have shared the same father!

He does feel something for me. . .he must, she thought dazedly. Surely, if all he wanted—all he'd ever wanted—was a casual affair, he would have gone merrily ahead and taken whatever she was prepared to offer and kept quiet about all this, ignored it?

Wouldn't he?

'You have a very strong-minded daughter, Charlotte,' Case said, looking chastened. 'I'll have to do my best to talk her round. My persuasive best.' He glanced at Avril, who'd been listening to all the revelations with a bemused fascination. 'I think we're more than ready for that cup of tea now, Avril, if you wouldn't mind.'

As Avril sprang to oblige Case turned back to Charlotte with a smile. His hand had somehow found Lucy's, and the warmth of his palm was flowing through her skin, heating her veins, making it hard for her to concentrate on what he was saying.

'This has been tough on you, Charlotte, I know,' he acknowledged in his deep, soft voice, 'but don't you feel better now that it's all out in the open at last? Now that you know my father kept your memory alive in his heart for the rest of his life?

'I hope you'll keep the brooch, which was created specially for you—I know, I checked with Kowalsky, only he wasn't able to tell me who the mysterious L in my father's life was. Take the brooch and the photograph of you that my father cherished until he died and remember how much you obviously meant to him. Even though he did the noble thing and put us—his family—first.'

'Thank you.' Charlotte's eyes misted again. 'I tried to hate him and forget him after he rejected me. . .he hurt me so much. But I never did stop loving him. Ever. And, yes, it does help to know that he kept my photograph, and the brooch he wanted to give me. I— I wouldn't accept it, I told him, until he was. . .free to give it to me. Thank you, Case. A lot of sons would have simply got rid of both and pretended they didn't exist.'

'If I'd thought you hadn't meant anything to my

father, I might have,' Case confessed with a rueful sigh. 'I admit it was curiosity in the beginning that drove me to want to find you, Charlotte. It intrigued me, knowing there was a woman out there somewhere who'd meant so much to my father that he'd kept her photograph and a valuable brooch obviously created for her.

'But then—' a softer light kindled deep in his eyes '—after I met and got to know your daughter, my need to meet you turned into something more than curiosity—far more. I knew I had to find out the truth before my feelings for her pulled me in any deeper. I had to be sure that my way was clear.' His eyes, darkly magnetic, sought Lucy's. 'I'm still not sure that it is. . . but I intend to work on the problem. From the moment we leave this house.'

Lucy found her gaze locked with his, felt herself drowning in the black depths as a delicious weakness spread through her. Was she imagining what she saw in his eyes? Could it possibly be true. . .that he wanted what she wanted. . .what she'd long dreamed of, fantasised about, but had never believed would ever happen?

Or was she going to wake up to reality with a jolt, like Cinderella, and find out that she'd been right all along, that men like Case Travers didn't marry unworldly, sports-mad suburban working girls. . .and that lasting love and marriage weren't even on his mind? Maybe all he wanted was an affair after all—perhaps a more romantic, longer-lasting, more meaningful affair than the fly-by-night kind he'd indulged in since his marriage break-up.

Her heart wavered. She would simply have to go along with it, savour whatever loving he could offer and bide her time. She would have to hope she could show him that real loving was. . .and convince him that he couldn't live without her. . .ever.

She blinked, reluctantly breaking the spell he was weaving over her. 'And what if—' she eyed him curiously '—you *had* been my half-brother?'

A flicker of something verging on real pain crossed his face. 'I would still have wanted you in my life, Lucy. I would have looked on you as a. . .sister, treated you as a sister. . .if you'd let me. If not, I would have found other ways of. . .looking out for you.'

'Here's Avril with our tea,' Charlotte put in gently, reminding them that they weren't alone.

They kept clear of delicate matters as they settled down to Avril's freshly baked scones and tea, keeping the conversation light. . .and safe.

Case made his farewells first, steering Avril out onto the veranda so that Lucy could bid her mother goodbye in private.

'Will you be all right, Mum?' Lucy asked anxiously.

'Of course, dear, I'll be fine.' Her mother hugged her. 'I know now that Nicholas did love me after all. . . just as he always said he did. And I loved him. . .so very much. I can say it now. He gave me a taste of what real love and complete happiness could be. . .even if ours didn't last for long. Only three short months. But every hour, every day of those twelve weeks was. . . precious, magical. I've always wanted *you* to know a love like that, darling. And I knew from the start that you didn't feel that kind of love for David.'

'Oh, Mum, I wish it could have been different for you—'

'Hush. A lot of people never know a love like that in their entire lives. But I hope that you will, darling.' Her gaze flickered to the partially open doorway. 'He loves you, Lucy. I've seen the way he looks at you. I saw the unbearable strain in his face when he asked if his father and I had met up again. . .later. He's obviously been going through hell, wondering just what was between us, wondering how long our affair lasted. He didn't use you, dear. I was wrong to accuse him of that, and so were you. He cares for you. . .very deeply. I've seen that look before. I know.'

Lucy, trembling at the words, smiled at her mother,

her eyes glistening with tears. Happy tears. 'You're not warning me about him any more? The suave, silver-tongued tycoon? The heartless womaniser? The type who plays fast and loose with women, who would never fall for a suburban working girl like Lucy Farrell? A divorced man, to boot?'

Her mother gave a rueful grimace and shook her head. 'I'm still not sure what his intentions are, precisely. That will be for you and Case to work out. All I know is that he loves you, dear. And that you. . .love him. But I *do* know what I'll be hoping. For both of you.'

'Oh, Mum, thanks for that. I—I wish you lived closer.'

'You never know. . .' Her mother's eyes twinkled suddenly. 'You might see me back in Melbourne yet. Avril's married daughter's coming home from overseas soon, to settle in Melbourne with her family, and I know that Avril would like to sell up and move back too, to be close to them. But she'll only go if I go with her.'

'Oh, Mum, that would be wonderful! Mike would love to have you back too. But. . .what about Dad and Beth? Would you—?'

'That wouldn't be a problem, dear. Your father and I parted good friends, remember. . .and I have no animosity towards Beth, nor she to me. Darling, you must go. Case is waiting.'

As Case pointed the car in the direction of Brisbane Airport Lucy felt a rush of nervous tension now that they were alone. To cover it, she went on the attack.

'I can't believe that all this time you thought. . .' She gave a bemused shake of her head. 'You're lucky my mother didn't slap your face. Accusing her of cheating on my father!'

Case glanced round, his lip twitching, his eyes growing tender as they collided with hers. 'Your mother understood that I had to ask.'

Lucy gave a snort. 'My brother Mike's barely two years older than I am. Did you truly believe that my mother would have had one child by her own husband and a daughter so soon afterwards by another man?'

Case shrugged, his eyes flicking back to the road. 'From what you'd told me about your parents, no... I didn't really believe it, even knowing they were divorced. But...I had to be sure. It was obvious that my father had loved your mother very deeply at one time, and you did tell me,' he reminded her, 'that you were nothing like your father. Martin Farrell. For all I knew, our parents could have met up again—even just once—after your mother was married to Martin.

'I can understand now—' he paused '—how passion can flare out of control.' His jaw clenched as he said it, his dark gaze still intent on the road in front. 'I never did understand,' he confessed, 'until I met you. Damn it, Lucy!' His voice roughened, his hand feeling for hers. 'You don't know how hard it's been.'

She shivered...a pleasurable ripple down her spine.

'Any other questions?' he asked a moment later, his voice light again, steadier. Now obviously wasn't the time to talk about passions. Not here on the open road, with a busy airport coming up.

She asked tentatively, 'Case...why didn't you show me my mother's photograph when you first met me? Why couldn't you have...trusted me?'

Case heaved a sigh. 'It wasn't a question of trust. It was a question of...delicacy. I knew nothing about you or your family back then, or what trouble or pain that photograph might cause. I had no idea how long your mother's relationship with my father had lasted, or how bringing it out into the open might affect your family. Besides, I didn't want to risk you rushing off and telling your mother about it. She might have clammed up... to protect *you* or herself...or she could have refused to see me, and then I might never have found out the truth.

'Anyway, it would have been wrong for me to speak to you first—to reveal a possible relationship between your mother and my father. It had to come from your mother. Added to that, I thought that if my father had sworn Charlotte to secrecy—which proved to be the case—I was the only one who could release your mother from her promise. So you see... I had to see her and speak to her myself.'

Lucy chewed on her lip. 'So...arranging for me to fly up to Brisbane with you during that pulp and paper conference had nothing to do with David...or wanting to reunite us?'

'Oh, yes, it had. Well, not wanting to reunite you so much, no. But I did want you to resolve your situation with David...and the quicker the better. Your mother, Lucy, wasn't the only reason I wanted to see more of you.' He was frowning ahead...as if looking for something. A turn-off? A sign? 'When we missed seeing your mother in Brisbane that time, I knew I'd have to put off finding out the truth until I could arrange another suitable time. For the three of us. Together.'

Lucy stifled a sigh. 'So you offered me a job...so that you'd be able to keep me around until you could.'

He shook his head. 'I did want you around...close to me...yes. But not for that reason. I just wanted you...close.' He glanced at her again, and she caught a heart-stopping gleam in the black depths of his eyes. 'Unfortunately, I couldn't get *too* close. Not until I knew the whole truth about my father's relationship with your mother. I asked you a lot of questions about your mother and your family, I admit it. Some answers I found reassuring...others kept the nagging doubts alive.'

'If you needed to know so badly, why didn't you simply fly up and see her yourself? You knew who she was by then, and where she lived.'

'Because I wanted *you* to get to know *me* better before I opened a possible Pandora's box. I wanted

you to learn to trust me, Lucy. . .to look on me as a. . .
friend. By that time I was beginning to feel things for
you that I. . .that complicated things, put it that way.
When I realised there was a vague possiblity that you
could be my half-sister, I knew I couldn't—mustn't—
go too far with you. Not until I knew for sure. In the
meantime, I wanted to keep you near me. I didn't want
to risk some other fellow snatching you away. When
you mentioned to me that your mother's birthday was
coming up, I knew that it would be a perfect opportunity to meet your mother. . .in a natural, non-con-
frontational way.'

'Poor Mum. Picking her birthday to spring her secret
past on her,' Lucy said musingly. 'For all you knew, it
could have shattered her and blown up in your face. In
all our faces.'

'I know,' he said heavily. 'That's why I said nothing
until this morning. I wasn't going to risk ruining her
birthday last night. Also, I wanted to give her a chance
to tell you herself. . .if what I feared was true. I was
sure that your mother, having seen how close you and
I had become, would be anxious to tell you if there was
any truth in what I feared.

'When it was obvious that she hadn't told you, I took
heart. But I still wasn't absolutely sure. . . I wanted you
to be there for your mother when I opened a possible
can of worms, and for you to have both of *us*—your
mother and I—there for you, to support you, reassure
you, console you. . .whatever might be needed. I didn't
intend to let you out of my life, Lucy Farrell. . .
whatever the truth turned out to be.'

As she swallowed hard, and wondered just what he
meant by not letting her out of his life, he suddenly
swung the car off the road into a petrol station, pulling
up not in front of the pumps but in a deserted parking
bay on the far side.

'What—what are you doing?' She swung round to
face him.

'This!' He twisted in his seat and dragged her into his arms, then kissed her as he'd never kissed her before, with a savage urgency combined with an overwhelming tenderness. She was left breathless, limp, her face flushed and beaded with sweat when he finally drew back.

'There's only one thing stopping me this time,' he said in a thick growl, his black eyes smouldering. 'The fact that we're in full view of a main highway. But when our plane, my lovely Lucy, touches down in Melbourne, I'm taking you straight to my head office building. . .straight up to my private penthouse. . . And we're going to spend the rest of the day and possibly all night long there. Alone.'

Flaming arrows speared down into the pit of her stomach, spreading a liquid heat all the way down her melting legs. But, weak as she felt, she was still able to summon a brief burst of spirit.

'I bet you say that to all the girls,' she breathed, hardly caring any more. Whatever he wanted of her, however long he intended to keep her in his life, why fight it any more? A few short weeks or months, even one rapturous night in Case Travers' arms would beat a lifetime spent with someone who loved her but could never make her feel like this.

She would grab whatever time, whatever happiness she could get. . .at the same time seizing the chance to show him how marvellously fulfilling life with her could be. She would make herself indispensable to him. . . make him see what living with someone who truly cared for him could be like. . . Until she realised he couldn't let her go. . .didn't ever want to let her go.

'Not any more, I don't,' he vowed, and she felt his hot breath and flicking tongue at her earlobe, an amazingly erotic sensation. 'Not since the day I first met you, my teasing tormentor. And never again from this day on, I swear.

'Remember what I said to you the other day? That I

was going to keep you in my life, one way or another? I meant either as a cherished sister, if that was the way it had to be, or. . .' He paused, burying his lips in her soft hair. 'Or as my *wife*.

'That's what I want, my darling. More than anything else I've ever wanted in my life or will ever want again. *You*, Lucy. . .having you with me. . .for always. Sharing my life with me. Sharing my bed. Sharing everything. From this day forward. Any children we are lucky enough to have will be icing on the cake. It's you I want. . .just you.'

'Oh, Case.' She melted into the curve of his shoulder, a rapturous smile on her lips. Her dreams had just come true. 'I feel like Cinderella. And you make the most wonderful prince. . .'

He wanted her, *loved* her, whether she gave him children or not. . .the children she knew he longed to have. 'And I know,' she whispered huskily, 'that you'll make a perfectly wonderful father too, Case. I hope our children are all like you.'

The look in his eyes rocked her to the depths, bringing a sparkle of tears to her eyes.

'And I hope,' he murmured hoarsely, 'that they're all like you, my delectable Cinderella. Good-looking, courageous, lovable, talented. . . Um, that reminds me. . .' A wicked gleam leapt to his eyes. 'I'd better check out your feet when we get home. Those succulent toes of yours must be in need of some urgent attention. . .some extra special attention.' He licked his lips.

She stifled a shiver of ecstasy to demand, 'Hey. . . who's the podiatrist around here. . .you or me? Feet— toes—are *my* domain.'

'Then maybe you'd better check out *my* toes?'

She feigned a shudder. 'You win. I don't mind reversing roles. . .just this once. Check out my toes all you like. Check out all of me.'

'It will be my pleasure.'

MILLS & BOON®

Next Month's Romances

♡

Each month you can choose from a wide variety of
romance novels from Mills & Boon. Below are the new
titles to look out for next month from the Presents and
Enchanted series.

Presents™

MISTAKEN FOR A MISTRESS	Jacqueline Baird
NIGHT OF SHAME	Miranda Lee
THE GUILTY WIFE	Sally Wentworth
LOOKING AFTER DAD	Elizabeth Oldfield
LOVERS' LIES	Daphne Clair
CLOSE RELATIONS	Lynsey Stevens
THE SEDUCTION TRAP	Sara Wood
HER PERSONAL BODYGUARD	Susan Mc Carthy

Enchanted™

THE DAUGHTER OF THE MANOR	Betty Neels
A BUSINESS ENGAGEMENT	Jessica Steele
RUNAWAY HONEYMOON	Ruth Jean Dale
McALLISTER'S BABY	Trisha David
BRIDE ON THE RANCH	Barbara McMahon
AMBER AND THE SHEIKH	Stephanie Howard
ONCE A COWBOY...	Day Leclaire
PRINCE OF DELIGHTS	Renee Roszel